CLASSICS *for* YOUNG READERS

Volume 5B

Editor: John Holdren

Art Director: Steve Godwin

Designer: Jayoung Cho

Illustrators:
Jayoung Cho
Vince McGinley
Deborah Wolfe, Ltd: (Jerry Dadds)

ISBN: 1-931728-43-7

Printed by Worzalla, Stevens Point, WI, USA, April 2014, Lot 042014

TABLE OF CONTENTS

STORIES FROM SHAKESPEARE

MYSTERY! ADVENTURES OF SHERLOCK HOLMES

FAVORITES FROM FAMOUS BOOKS:
LITTLE WOMEN

LIFE STORIES: YOUNG AND BRAVE

POETRY

NO MATTER WHERE IT'S GOING

AMERICAN THEMES

STORIES FROM SHAKESPEARE

A MIDSUMMER NIGHT'S DREAM
based on the play by William Shakespeare

1

Once upon a time, and a long ago time it was, there was in the city of Athens a severe law. This law said that a daughter must marry the man her father chose for her—and, if the daughter refused to marry the chosen man, then the father could have her put to death. Now, as fathers generally do not desire the death of even the most stubborn of daughters, this law was never enforced.

But in the days when Theseus was Duke of Athens, there came to his court an angry and excited old man named Egeus. He dragged behind him his lovely daughter, Hermia. "O noble Duke!" cried Egeus. "Full of vexation I come, with complaint against my child. I ask for justice! I claim the law of Athens against my daughter."

"Why so, Egeus?" asked the duke.

"Because, renowned Duke," answered Egeus, "the law says that a daughter must marry the man her father chooses, or else suffer death. I have chosen Demetrius, but she will not have him. And why? Because her heart has been stolen by young Lysander. With rhymes, bracelets, trinkets, and nosegays, he has filched my daughter's heart, and turned her obedience, which is due to me. I crave permission to enforce the law. Either to Demetrius she must go in marriage, or to her death!"

Then Theseus turned to the daughter and asked, "What have you to say, Hermia? Demetrius is a worthy gentleman."

"So is Lysander," replied Hermia.

"In himself he is," said Theseus, "but he lacks your father's approval. And so the other must be held worthier."

"I would rather my father looked with my eyes," said Hermia.

"Rather," advised Theseus, "your eyes must look with his judgment."

"O noble Duke!" pleaded Hermia. "Demetrius formerly loved my friend Helena. She did return his love and still devoutly dotes upon him. And yet, he has turned from her to me. How can I trust such a man? I do not love him. I love Lysander, and Lysander loves me."

The duke's heart was deeply moved at this plea. He was a merciful ruler, and great, but even he could not alter the laws of Athens. Therefore he said, "Hermia, I am sorry for you, but all I can do is give you four days to consider. If at the end of that time your father has not changed his mind, you must either marry Demetrius or be put to death. That is the law, and I cannot change it."

When they had left the duke's presence, Hermia immediately sought Lysander and told him of the danger she was in. "I must either give you up, Lysander, and marry Demetrius," she said, "or lose my life in four days."

Lysander was in great sorrow at hearing Hermia's tidings. "Ay me," he cried. "In all the books that I have ever read, the course of true love never did run smooth."

"Oh," wailed Hermia, "that I must choose love by another's eyes!"

Lysander took her hand and said, "Hear me, Hermia. I have an aunt, a wealthy widow, who lives far from Athens." He explained that where his aunt lived, the cruel Athenian law could not affect them. So he proposed to Hermia that she should steal out of her father's house that night, and go with him to his aunt's house, where he would marry her. "I will meet you," said Lysander, "in the wood a few miles outside the city, where we have sometimes walked with Helena."

Hermia joyfully agreed to Lysander's proposal. She told no one of her intended flight except her dear friend Helena. To her she confided all their plans, ending with these words:

> "And in the wood, where often you and I
> Upon faint primrose beds were wont to lie,
> Emptying our bosoms of their counsel sweet,
> There my Lysander and myself shall meet.
> And thence from Athens turn away our eyes,
> To seek new friends and stranger companies."

As Helena waved farewell, she began to think. And her thoughts took a foolish and ungenerous turn. "Throughout Athens," she said to herself, "I am thought as fair as Hermia. But what of that? Demetrius thinks not so. He dotes on Hermia's eyes. Though once, before he looked on her, he swore that he was only mine. I will go tell him of fair Hermia's flight!"

And so she did—though she knew she had nothing to gain by betraying Hermia's secret but the poor pleasure of following the faithless Demetrius to the wood, where he was sure to pursue Hermia.

2

This wood in which Lysander and Hermia were to meet was the favorite haunt of those little beings known as fairies. Oberon, the king of the fairies, and Titania, the queen, with all their tiny followers, held their midnight revels in this wood. When the moon shone, the lovely dells and glades, all carpeted with moss and flowers, were filled with tiny forms clad in gossamer, dancing in joyous measure to merry music.

But at this time there happened to be a sad disagreement between Oberon and Titania. Whenever they met in the shady walks of this pleasant wood, they quarreled so fiercely that all the other fairies and sprites would creep into acorn cups and hide themselves for fear.

The cause of this unhappy disagreement was that Titania refused to give to Oberon a little changeling boy. The mother of this boy had been Titania's friend; and upon her death, the fairy queen took the child and brought him up in the wood. But Oberon wanted the child for his own.

It was now the night on which Lysander and Hermia were to meet in the wood. Titania was out walking with her maids, and they chanced to meet Oberon, attended by his little men.

"Ill met by moonlight, proud Titania," said the fairy king.

"What, jealous Oberon! Is it you?" the queen replied. "Fairies, skip hence. I have forsworn his company."

"Tarry, rash fairy," said Oberon. "Am I not thy lord? Why does Titania cross her Oberon? Give me your little changeling boy to be my page."

"Set your heart at rest," answered the queen. "Your whole fairy kingdom buys not the boy from me." She then left her lord in great anger.

"Well! Go your way," said Oberon. "Before the morning dawns, I will torment you for this injury."

Oberon then sent for the shrewd and knavish sprite named Robin Goodfellow, but better known as Puck. Puck was Oberon's favorite. He delighted in mischief and pranks.

"Come hither, Puck," said Oberon to this merry little wanderer of the night. "Fetch me the flower which maids call 'Love in Idleness.' If the juice of that little purple flower be laid on the eyelids of those who sleep, it will make them, when they awake, fall in love with the first thing they see. Some of the juice of that flower I will drop on the eyelids of my Titania when she is asleep. The first thing she looks upon when she opens her eyes, she will dote upon, though it be a lion, a bear, or wolf, or a meddling monkey, or a busy ape. Before I take this charm off her sight, I will make her give me that boy to be my page."

Puck, who loved mischief with all his heart, was highly pleased with this scheme of his master, and sped to seek the flower.

While Oberon was awaiting the return of Puck, he saw Demetrius and Helena enter the wood. He overheard Demetrius speak unkind words to Helena, who had eagerly followed him.

"Get thee gone, and follow me no more," Demetrius barked at Helena. "In plainest truth I tell you, I do not and cannot love you."

"And even for that do I love you the more," cried Helena. "Spurn me, neglect me, only let me follow you, unworthy as I am."

Demetrius turned and ran, and Helena ran after him as swiftly as she could.

As the fairy king watched them run away, he smiled. "Lady," he said softly, "before this night is over, he shall seek thy love, and thou shalt flee from him!"

At this moment, Puck returned with the little purple flower. "Welcome, wanderer," said Oberon. "Take part of the flower, and seek through this grove. There has been a sweet Athenian lady here, who is in love with a disdainful youth. When you find him sleeping, drop some of the love juice into his eyes. But do it when she is near him, so that she may be the first thing he sees when he awakes. You will know the man by the Athenian garments he wears."

Puck promised to manage this matter very skillfully, and away he went. Then Oberon slyly went to seek his queen in her fairy bower.

He found her preparing to go to rest, on a bank of wild flowers. "Come now," Titania said to her fairies. "Some of you must kill cankers in the musk-rose buds. And some must wage war with the bats for their leathery wings to make my small elves' coats. And some of you keep watch that the clamorous owl come not near me. Sing me now asleep, and let me rest."

Then the fairies began to sing this song:

> *"You spotted snakes with double tongue,*
> *Thorny hedgehogs be not seen;*
> *Newts and blindworms, do no wrong,*
> *Come not near our fairy queen.*
>
> *Philomel, with melody,*
> *Sing in our sweet lullaby;*
> *Lulla, lulla, lullaby; lulla, lulla, lullaby.*
> *Never harm, nor spell, nor charm,*
> *Come our lovely lady nigh;*
> *So, good night with lullaby."*

When the fairies had sung their queen asleep, they left her to do what she had ordered. Then Oberon softly drew near and dropped some of the love juice on Titania's eyelids, saying,

> *"What thou seest when thou dost wake,*
> *Do it for thy true love take.*
> *In thy eye, it shall appear*
> *When thou wak'st, it is thy dear:*
> *Wake when some vile thing is near."*

3

While all this was taking place, Hermia made her escape from her father's house and ran to the wood. There she met Lysander, who was waiting to guide her to his aunt's house. Off they went through the moonlit shadows. But before they had passed through half the wood, Hermia became so tired that she could go no farther. Lysander persuaded her to rest till morning on a bank of soft moss. Then, leaving a good distance between them, he found a place to lie on the ground, and he, too, soon fell asleep.

As Hermia and Lysander slept, who should come by but mischievous Puck? Puck, as you know, had been sent by Oberon to seek Demetrius. But Oberon had told Puck that he would recognize the man by his Athenian garments. As Puck looked at the sleeping form of Lysander, he said, "Who is here? Clothes of Athens he doth wear." Puck was sure that this must be the scornful young man Oberon had sent him to seek. So he let some of the love juice from the flower drip into Lysander's eyes. "So awake when I am gone," whispered Puck, "for I must now to Oberon."

As Puck left, he did not see a woman come wandering to the very place where Lysander was sleeping. This was Helena. She had lost sight of Demetrius, who had run from her so rudely and so swiftly. And now, in the darkness, alone, she almost stumbled across Lysander's sleeping form.

"Ah," she cried, "this is Lysander, lying on the ground! Is he dead or asleep?" Then, gently touching him, she said, "Good sir, if you are alive, awake!"

Upon this Lysander opened his eyes, and the first person he saw was Helena. The charm did its work. "Sweet Helena," he breathed, "I would run through fire for thy sake."

Helena was confused. "Do not say so, Lysander," she protested. "Hermia still loves you. Be content."

But Lysander took her hand and said with great urgency, "Not Hermia, but Helena I love. Who will not change a raven for a dove?"

Helena knew that Lysander was solemnly pledged to marry Hermia, so she thought he was making fun of her. "Oh," said she, "why was I born to be mocked and scorned by everyone? Is it not enough that I can never get a sweet look or a kind word from Demetrius? And now you, sir, must pretend thus to love me? Lysander, I thought you were a lord of more true gentleness."

Saying these words in great anger, she ran away. Lysander followed her, quite forgetful of Hermia, who was still asleep.

When Hermia awoke she was frightened to find herself alone. She wandered through the wood, not knowing what had become of Lysander or which way to go to seek him.

In the meantime Demetrius, who had fled from Helena, had run back and forth, hither and yon, seeking Hermia and Lysander. But he had not been able to find them. At last, tired out with his fruitless search, he lay down in a clearing and fell fast asleep.

By this time, Oberon had realized Puck's mistake, and was in search of the right man to charm. As he came upon the sleeping Demetrius, Oberon turned to Puck and said, "Go now, softer than the wind, and find Helena, and see thou bring her here. I'll charm his eyes before she does appear."

In a flash, Puck went in search of Helena, while Oberon leaned over Demetrius and chanted,

> "Flower of this purple dye,
> Hit with Cupid's archery.
> When his love he doth espy,
> Let her shine as gloriously
> As the Venus of the sky."

Oberon touched the eyelids of Demetrius with the love juice, just as Puck reappeared to report, "Captain of our fairy land, Helena is here at hand."

Oberon and his sprite hurried away. Demetrius awoke, and the first person he saw passing by was Helena. "O Helena," he sighed, "goddess, nymph, perfect, divine!"

At this very moment Lysander came running into the clearing, with Hermia running after. Then Lysander and Demetrius both turned to Helena and, speaking at the same time, praised her charms and vowed their love for her.

"What does all this mean?" cried Helena. "Why are you thus making sport of me?"

Then she turned to Hermia. "Unkind Hermia," she said, "it is you who have set Lysander on to vex me with mock praises. It is you who have told your Demetrius to call me a goddess. He would not speak thus if you did not set him on. Have you forgotten our friendship? Hermia, it is not kind to join with men in scorning your poor friend."

"I am amazed at your words," answered Hermia. "I do not scorn you, but it seems that you scorn me."

"Ay, keep on with your pretense," returned Helena. "When I turn my back, wink at each other and keep up the sport. If you had any pity, grace, or manners, Hermia, you would not use me thus."

Helena and Hermia were not the only ones exchanging angry words. A little way apart, Demetrius and Lysander argued over the love of Helena. Their words became so heated that they slipped away into the wood to fight each other for Helena's love. When the women discovered that the men had left them, they departed and once more wandered wearily in the wood to search for them.

As soon as they were gone, the fairy king, Oberon—who, with Puck, had been listening to their quarrels—turned to the little sprite and said, "You heard that Demetrius and Lysander are gone to seek a place to fight. I command you to overhang the night with a thick fog, and to lead these quarrelsome lovers so astray in the dark that they shall not be able to find each other. Imitate each of their voices and provoke them to follow you. See that you do this till they are so weary that they can go no farther. When you find they are asleep, drop the juice of this other flower in Lysander's eyes. When he awakes, he will forget his new love for Helena, and return to his old passion for Hermia. Go about this quickly, Puck, and I will go and see what sweet love my Queen Titania has found."

Then Puck sped away, singing as he went,

> "Up and down, up and down,
>   I will lead them up and down;
>   I am feared in field and town:
>   Goblin, lead them up and down."

4

Now you might think that with all these mix-ups, there would be no place for any more mischief in the wood this night. But mischief was brewing, not far away, where a crew of Athenian workmen had entered the wood to practice a play. They came with all good intentions, for they hoped to perform their play during the celebrations of the upcoming wedding of Duke Theseus.

While their intentions were good, their acting, alas, was bad. And he who thought himself the best actor—Nick Bottom, the weaver—was in fact the worst. Nevertheless, this did not stop him from offering to play all the parts, nor from giving much advice to his fellow workmen.

It happened that the play called for one man to play the part of a lion. "Let me play the lion!" cried Bottom, though he had already stood forth to play both the hero and the heroine. "I will roar so that it will do any man's heart good to hear me. Why, when I roar, the Duke will say, 'Let him roar again! Let him roar again!'"

"Nay," said Peter Quince the carpenter, "for if you should do it too terrible, you would frighten the ladies."

"Well then," replied Bottom, "I will roar as gently as a baby dove. I will roar like a nightingale." Apparently, Bottom had not considered what effect might be made upon an audience by a lion that roared like a nightingale.

In the end, it was decided that Bottom must play the hero, a tragic figure named Pyramus in a play curiously titled *The Most Lamentable Comedy and Most Cruel Death of Pyramus and Thisby.* After each man was assigned a role, they walked apart to study their lines.

It was thus, while Bottom wandered alone in the woods, that he was spied by none other than Puck. "What have we swaggering here?" said Puck. Then the mischief rose in him, and he could not resist casting a little spell on Bottom.

When Bottom returned to his fellows, they stared at him in horror. "O Bottom!" they cried, "thou art changed. O monstrous! O strange! Help! Run!"

"Why do you run away?" cried Bottom—for he could not see himself, and therefore did not know that Puck had given him the head of a donkey.

"I see what you are up to," cried Bottom. "You mean to frighten me. You mean to make a jackass of me! Well, I will walk up and down here and sing. That will show them that I am not afraid."

And so Bottom walked and sang, in a voice not unlike a donkey's braying. As he sang and walked, he chanced upon the bower where Titania, the fairy queen, lay sleeping.

At that very moment Titania opened her eyes and beheld the donkey-headed man. The juice of the little purple flower had taken effect. She cried out, "What angel wakes me from my flowery bed? Are you as wise as you are beautiful?"

"Why, mistress," said Nick Bottom, "if I have wit enough to find the way out of this wood, I have enough to serve my turn."

"Out of the wood, do not desire to go," said the lovesick queen. "I am a spirit of no common kind. I love you. Go with me, and I will give you fairies to attend upon you."

Titania then called four of her fairies: Pease-blossom, Cobweb, Moth, and Mustard-seed. To them she said, "Attend upon this sweet gentleman. Feed him with grapes and apricots, and steal for him the honey bags from the bees."

Then the fairy queen sighed to Bottom, "Come, sit with me, and let me play with your amiable hairy cheeks, and let me kiss your fair large ears, my gentle joy!"

"Where is Pease-blossom?" asked donkey-headed Nick Bottom, very proud of his new attendants.

"Here, sir," answered little Pease-blossom.

"Scratch my head," said Bottom. "Where is Cobweb?"

"Here, sir," answered Cobweb.

"Good Mr. Cobweb," said foolish Bottom, "chase away the red bumblebee on top of that thistle yonder, and bring me the honey bag. Do not fret yourself too much in the action, Mr. Cobweb, and take care the honey bag break not. I should be sorry to have you overflowed with honey. Now, where is Mustard-seed?"

"Here, sir," answered Mustard-seed. "What is your will?"

"Nothing, good Mr. Mustard-seed," replied Bottom, "but to help Mr. Pease-blossom to scratch. I must go to a barber, Mr. Mustard-seed, for methinks I am marvelous hairy about the face."

"My sweet love," said the queen, "what will you have to eat? I have a bold fairy who shall seek the squirrel's hoard and fetch you some new nuts."

"I had rather have a handful of dried peas," said Bottom, who had got a donkey's appetite with his donkey's head. "But, I pray, let none of your people disturb me, for I have a mind to sleep."

"Sleep, then," said the queen, "and I will wind you in my arms. Oh, how I love you! How I dote upon you!"

When Oberon saw the donkey-headed man sleeping in the arms of Titania, he advanced within her sight and again demanded the changeling boy. This time, so blinded was Titania by the juice of the magic flower to everything but her newfound love, she readily gave up the little boy.

Now that Oberon had obtained the boy he had so long wished to be his page, he took pity on poor Titania. He threw some of the juice of the other flower into her eyes, and spoke these words:

> *"Be as thou wast wont to be;*
> *See as thou wast wont to see:*
> *Now, my Titania; wake you, my sweet queen."*

The fairy queen shook her head, as though she were coming out of a daze. Then, spying the fairy king, she said, "My Oberon, what visions I have seen. I thought I was in love with a jackass!"

Oberon pointed to Bottom, sleeping soundly, and said, "There lies your love."

"Oh, how I do hate to look upon him now!" Titania cried.

"Silence a while," said Oberon. Then he ordered Puck to remove the donkey head. Puck did so, and left Bottom to finish his nap with his own fool's head upon his shoulders.

"Come, my queen, take hands with me," said Oberon to Titania. Then he told her of Demetrius and Lysander, and Hermia and Helena, and the various mix-ups, and the midnight quarrels in the wood. She agreed to go with him and see the end of their adventures.

5

The fairy king and queen found the men and the ladies sleeping on the grass. Puck had managed to bring them all to the same spot, unknown to each other because of the thick fog. And he had carefully removed the charm from the eyes of Lysander.

Hermia awoke first. Finding her lost Lysander asleep nearby, she kept looking at him and wondering at his strange conduct. Soon Lysander opened his eyes, and seeing his dear Hermia, recovered his reason, which the fairy charm had before clouded. And with his reason, he recovered also his love for Hermia.

They began to talk over the adventures of the night. They wondered whether these strange things had really happened, or if they had both been dreaming the same bewildering dream.

Helena and Demetrius were by this time awake. Sweet sleep had quieted Helena's angry spirits, so she listened with delight to Demetrius. "My love for Hermia is melted as the snow," he said, "and the pleasure of my eye is only Helena."

The ladies became once more true friends. All the unkind words that had passed between them were forgiven.

As they prepared to return to Athens, they were all surprised at the sight of Egeus, Hermia's father, who had come to the wood in search of his runaway daughter. With him came Duke Theseus.

When Egeus saw Hermia hand in hand with Lysander, he cried out, "Enough, enough, my lord! They would have stolen away! I beg the law upon them!"

But then Demetrius spoke. "My lord," he explained, "I know not by what power—for by some power it is—but all my love for Hermia has melted as the snow. And the object and pleasure of my eye is only Helena. I will for evermore be true to her."

"Egeus," said the duke, "I will overrule your will. In the temple, by and by, these couples shall eternally be knit."

So the cruel sentence of death, which had threatened Hermia, was taken away, and she was happily married instead. On the same day Helena was married to her beloved, the now faithful Demetrius. The wedding bells rang merrily and every living soul was happy.

The fairy king and queen, who had together watched over the whole affair, were so delighted that they celebrated the weddings of these mortals by sports and revels throughout their fairy kingdom.

And now if there are any who think this story of fairies and pranks is too strange to be true, they have only to think that they have been asleep and dreaming a pretty, harmless Midsummer Night's Dream.

THE TEMPEST

based on the play by William Shakespeare

1

On an island in the midst of the sea, there lived, many hundred years ago, an old man named Prospero, and his beautiful daughter Miranda. They had been cast upon this island when Miranda was so young that she had no memory of any other human face than her father's. They were the only human beings on the whole island.

Their home was a cave hollowed out of a rock. It was divided into several rooms, one of which Prospero called his study. Here Prospero kept his books, which he loved to read and ponder. From these books he learned magic—not the dark ways of evil sorcerers, but the strong and secret powers of nature, which, after long study, he had turned to the uses of his own art.

This was no ordinary island, for it had once been enchanted by a witch called Sycorax, who died there a short time before Prospero arrived. Before she died, this cruel witch had imprisoned a good spirit in the trunk of a large tree, because he had refused to obey her wicked commands. By his magical art, Prospero had released this gentle spirit from its dark prison. And now Ariel, as this lively sprite was called, was obedient to Prospero, and carried out his commands quickly and skillfully.

Also living on the island was a strange, misshapen monster called Caliban, the son of the old witch Sycorax.

Prospero had found this beast-like creature lurking in the woods. He had taken Caliban home to his cave in the rock, had taught him to speak, and had tried to be very kind to him. Caliban had even become little Miranda's playmate, and she had tried to teach him many good and useful things.

But it proved too late to transform the monster's dark and corrupt nature. He was ungrateful, and his actions turned wicked, and finally Prospero had no choice but to turn him out. Then Caliban was required to fetch the wood and the water, to make the fires, and to do other kinds of hard work.

Caliban hated to work. And he hated Prospero, whose knowledge and power were so much greater than Caliban could ever hope to attain. The monster wanted the island to himself. He wanted to lie all day in the sun and watch the clouds and insects. So he would neglect his work. And then Ariel, who was invisible to all eyes but Prospero's, would come and pinch him, or tumble him down in the mire.

After Prospero and Miranda had lived alone on the island for many years, there came one day a violent storm. Jagged streaks of lightning ripped the sky. Thunder cracked and roared. The waves of the sea rose high as the black clouds, and then pounded down with wild fury.

In the midst of this storm, Prospero and Miranda watched as a fine, large ship struggled against the wild sea waves that every moment threatened to swallow it up.

"My dearest father," cried Miranda, "if by your art you have put the wild waters in this roar, calm them! See, the brave vessel will be dashed to pieces! Poor souls, they will all perish! If I had the power, I would sink the sea within the earth, rather than let the good ship be destroyed and all the noble souls within her."

"Be not amazed, my daughter," said Prospero. "There is no harm done. I have ordered all so safely that no person in the ship shall receive any hurt. What I have done has been done in care of you, my dear one. For you know not who you are, nor whence we came. You know no more of me than that I am your father, and live in this poor cave on this lonely island. Can you remember a time before we came unto this cell? I do not think you can, for you were not then three years old."

"Certainly, sir, I can," replied Miranda.

"What can you remember, my child?" asked Prospero. "What other house or person?"

Miranda thought for a moment and replied, "It seems to me more like a dream than like remembering the past. Had I not once four or five women who attended upon me?"

"You had," Prospero answered, "and more. How is it that this still lives in your mind? Do you also remember how you came here?"

"No, sir," said Miranda, "I remember nothing more."

"Then the time has come," her father said, "when you must hear the story. Twelve years ago, Miranda, I was the duke of Milan, and you were a princess and my only heir. I had a younger brother, Antonio, whom, next to you, I loved most dearly. I trusted him to represent me. He was so skillful in governing the state that, gradually, I neglected my affairs, and buried myself among the books that I love. As my brother exercised my power, he began to think of himself as the duke. His ambitions grew. He began to dream of depriving me of my dukedom. And this he soon did with the aid of Alonso, the king of Naples, who was my enemy. One dark night they took me from my palace, me and my crying child, and hurried us out of the city."

"Wherefore," asked Miranda, "did they not destroy us?"

"My child," answered her father, "they did not dare, for the people did love me dearly. They carried us on board a ship, and when we were some leagues out at sea, they forced us into a little old boat, without sail or mast, so rotten the very rats had deserted it. There they left us, as they thought, to perish. But a noble lord of my court, named Gonzalo, had secretly placed in the boat water, food, clothes, and some books that I prize above my dukedom."

"O my father," said Miranda, "what a trouble must I have been to you then!"

"No, my love," said Prospero, "you were an angel that did preserve me. Your innocent smiles made me bear up against my misfortunes. Our food lasted till we landed on this island.

Since then, Miranda, I have taught you much, and you have profited well by my instructions."

"Heaven thank you, dear father," said Miranda. "Now pray tell me, sir, your reason for raising this sea-storm."

"Know then," replied her father, "that by means of this storm my enemies, Alonso, the king of Naples, and Antonio, my cruel brother, are cast ashore upon this island."

Just then Ariel presented himself before his master to give an account of the tempest, and to tell what had been done with the ship's company. With a gentle spell, Prospero caused his daughter to fall into a sweet sleep, so that he might speak with Ariel, as he always did, in private.

"Approach my Ariel," called Prospero.

"All hail, great master, grave sir, hail!" replied Ariel in greeting. "'Tis Ariel's task to do thy strong bidding, be it to fly, to swim, to dive into the fire, or to ride on the curled clouds."

"Hast thou, spirit," asked Prospero, "performed the task I gave thee?"

"In every way," responded Ariel. And he proceeded to tell how he flashed lightning about the ship, and made the thunder crack, and the waves rise and fall. He described the terror of the mariners, and how they leaped into the sea.

"But Ariel," asked Prospero, "are they safe?"

"Not a hair perished," said Ariel, "and, as thou told me, I have dispersed them in groups about the isle." He then told how the king's son, Ferdinand, plunged into the foaming brine, and how the king, seeing his dear son swallowed by the waves, thought him lost forever.

"But he is safe," said Ariel, "in a corner of the isle. He is sitting with his arms folded, sadly lamenting the loss of his father, for he thinks his father was drowned. Not a hair of

Ferdinand's head is injured, and his garments, though drenched, look fresher than before."

"Why, that's my spirit!" said Prospero. "Bring him hither. My daughter must see this young prince. Where is the king, and where is my brother?"

"I left them," answered Ariel, "searching for Ferdinand, whom they have little hope of finding, because they think they saw him perish. Of the ship's crew, all are saved. And the ship, though invisible to them, is safe in the harbor. The rest of the fleet have all met again and are sailing sadly back to Naples, for they think they saw the king's ship wrecked and the great king perish."

"Ariel," said Prospero, "your charge is faithfully performed. But there is more work to do."

"Is there more toil?" exclaimed Ariel. "Let me remind you, master, that you have promised me my liberty. Remember, I pray, that I have done you worthy service, told you no lies, made no mistakes, and served you without grudge or grumbling."

"Do you forget," asked Prospero, "from what a torment I freed you?"

"I do not forget," said Ariel.

"I say you do! Have you forgotten the foul witch Sycorax, bent double with age and envy? "

"No, sir," answered Ariel.

"Ay, sir! You were her servant. And because you would not carry out her wicked commands, she shut you up in a cloven trunk of a pine tree. You had been there twelve years when I found you groaning. Was it not my art that made the pine tree open and let you out?"

"I thank you, master."

"If you murmur again, I will rend an oak, and peg you inside till you have howled away another twelve winters."

"Pardon, master," said Ariel. "I will obey your commands."

"Do so," answered Prospero, "and after two days I will set you free."

"That's my noble master!" cried Ariel. "What shall I do?"

Prospero gave his orders, and away went Ariel, swift and invisible as the wind.

2

First Ariel went to where he had left the king's son, Ferdinand. He found the young man still mourning for his father.

"Oh, my young gentleman," thought Ariel, when he saw him, "I will soon move you. You must be brought to the Lady Miranda." So Ariel began to sing:

> "Full fathom five thy father lies;
>   Of his bones are coral made;
> Those are pearls that were his eyes;
>   Nothing of him that doth fade,
> But doth suffer a sea-change
> Into something rich and strange.
> Sea-nymphs hourly ring his knell:
> Hark! Now I hear them—ding-dong, bell."

This strange song roused the prince. "Where does this music come from?" he cried. "This is no earthly sound." And in amazement he followed the sound of Ariel's voice, till it led him to the place where Prospero and Miranda were sitting under the shade of a large tree.

"Miranda," said Prospero, pointing to Ferdinand, "look over there and tell me what you see."

"Oh, father!" cried Miranda in surprise. "Is it a spirit? How it looks about! Is it not a spirit, father?"

"No, child," answered her father, gently, for he remembered that she had never seen a young man before. "It eats, and sleeps, and has such senses as we have. This is a young man that you see. He was in the ship, and is now wandering about to find his lost companions. He is somewhat changed by grief, or you might call him a handsome person."

"I might call him a thing divine, for nothing so noble have I ever seen," said Miranda. She had supposed that all men must have grave faces and gray beards like her father. So she was delighted with the appearance of this beautiful young prince.

Seeing this, Prospero turned aside and whispered to Ariel, "It goes as I wish. Spirit, fine spirit, I'll free thee within two days for this."

As for Ferdinand, he looked in wonder upon Miranda and her father—but most of all, upon Miranda. "Surely," he said to Miranda, "you must be the goddess of this place."

She timidly answered that she was no goddess, but a simple maid. Just then Prospero broke in. He was well pleased to find that they admired each other. But he knew that so swift an affection might prove light and brief. So he resolved to test Ferdinand and throw some difficulties in their way.

Prospero addressed the prince sternly, saying, "You have put yourself upon this island as a spy, to win it from me, the lord on it."

"No, as I am a man, I have not," answered Ferdinand.

"Follow me, traitor," said Prospero. "I will tie your neck and feet together. You shall drink sea-water. Withered roots and husks of acorns shall be your food."

"No," declared Ferdinand, "I will resist till I see a more powerful enemy."

Ferdinand drew his sword, but Prospero raised his staff and fixed the prince to the spot where he stood, so that he had no power to move.

Miranda hung upon her father, saying, "Why are you so ungentle? Have pity, sir! This is but the third man I ever saw, and to me he seems a true one."

"Silence!" said her father. "One word more will make me chide you. What! You think there are no more such men, having seen only him and Caliban. I tell you, foolish girl, most men as far excel this one as he does Caliban."

"Come on, young man," said Prospero to the prince. "You have no power to disobey me."

"I have not, indeed," answered Ferdinand. "But if, from my prison, I might behold this maid but once a day, then I will have space enough."

Ferdinand did not remain long in his cell, for Prospero ordered him to pile logs in front of the cave that was their home. Kings' sons are not used to such heavy work, and when Miranda approached, she found Ferdinand almost exhausted. "Alas," said she, "do not work so hard! Pray, rest yourself!"

"Oh, my dear lady," said Ferdinand, "I dare not! I must finish my task before I take my rest."

"If you will sit down," said Miranda, "I will carry your logs for you."

"No, dear creature," said Ferdinand. "I had rather crack my back than have you undergo such dishonor while I sit lazily by."

"It would suit me as well as you," said Miranda. "You look so weary."

"No, noble mistress," replied Ferdinand. "It is fresh morning with me when you are by at night."

They began to talk gently to each other, and the work of log-carrying went on very slowly indeed. Unknown to them and unseen by them, Prospero looked on. He would have been very angry if he had really wanted the logs piled. But he had set Ferdinand at this task merely as a trial.

He was glad to see that Ferdinand thought Miranda the most beautiful woman in all the world. When he overheard them declare their love for each other, he said to himself,

"Fair encounter of two most rare affections!" And he smiled with satisfaction when Ferdinand told Miranda that he was heir to the crown of Naples, and that she should be his queen.

Miranda was so delighted with Ferdinand that, without waiting for her father's consent, she told him that she would be his wife. Later Prospero called them to him, and instead of censuring them, said, "Ferdinand, all my vexations were but my trials of your love, and you have passed the test. If I have too severely used you, I will make you rich amends by giving you my daughter in marriage."

Prospero left them to sit and talk together till he returned. He then called Ariel, who quickly appeared before him, eager to relate what he had done with Prospero's brother, Antonio, and the king of Naples.

Ariel said he had left them almost out of their senses with fear at the strange things he had caused them to see and hear. When they were tired with wandering, and famished for want of food, he suddenly set before them a delicious banquet. But just as they were going to eat, he took shape before them in the shape of a disgusting monster with wings and claws, and the feast vanished.

Then to their utter amazement, Ariel, in his monstrous shape, spoke to them. "Remember," he screeched, "that you from Milan did supplant good Prospero, and exposed him and his innocent child unto the sea. For this foul deed, the powers have angered the seas and shores—yea, all the creatures against your peace."

Then, trembling with fear and shame, they saw how evil their deeds had been, and they repented of the injustice they had done to Prospero.

All this Ariel reported to Prospero. "And if you now beheld them," Ariel added, "you would pity them, and your feelings would become tender."

"Do you think so, spirit?" asked Prospero.

"Mine would, sir, if I were human."

"Then bring them hither, Ariel. If you, who are not human, feel for their distress, shall not I, who am a human being like themselves, be more kindly to them? Bring them quickly, my dainty Ariel."

Ariel returned to the king, Antonio, and old Gonzalo. This Gonzalo was the same nobleman who had so kindly provided Prospero with water and food and books, when his wicked brother Antonio left him to perish in an open boat in the sea. The three men followed Ariel, wondering at the strange music the invisible spirit played to draw them on to his master's presence.

In grief and terror, the three men stopped before Prospero, who used his power to make them stand mute and still. He first spoke to the good old Gonzalo. "Holy Gonzalo, honorable man, my true preserver!"

Then to the king of Naples he said, "Most cruelly didst thou use me and my daughter."

Then to Antonio he said, "Flesh and blood, brother mine, you would have killed your king. I do forgive thee, unnatural though thou art."

Antonio begged his brother's forgiveness. The king said he was sincerely sorry for the injustice done by them both, and promised to give the dukedom back to Prospero.

Then Prospero said to the king, "Since you have given me my dukedom again, I will repay you with as good a thing." He led them to look through a door, where they could see

Miranda playing a game of chess with the king's son, Ferdinand. Nothing could exceed the joy of the father and the son at this unexpected meeting, for each had thought the other drowned in the storm.

Miranda was not less surprised at seeing so many people on the island where, for so many years, she had been alone with her father. "O wonder!" she exclaimed. "How many goodly creatures are there here! How beauteous mankind is! O brave new world that has such people in it!"

The king of Naples was as much astonished at the beauty and grace of Miranda as his son had been. "Who is this maid?" asked he. "She seems to be the goddess that parted us, and now has brought us together again."

"No, sir," answered Ferdinand, smiling to find that his father had fallen into the same mistake he made when he first saw Miranda. "She is no goddess; she is a mortal. She is the daughter of Prospero, the famous duke of Milan, who gave me a second life. I chose her for my wife when I could not ask for your consent, thinking you were not alive."

"Then I must be a father to her," said the king, "and I must ask my child forgiveness."

Prospero had more good news for them. Their ship, he said, was returned and safe in the harbor, with the sailors all on board. And the next morning, he added, he and his daughter would board the ship and accompany them to Naples, where Miranda and Ferdinand would be wed.

"In the meantime," said he, "partake of such refreshments as my poor cave affords. And for your evening's entertainment I will relate the history of my life from my first landing on this island."

Before Prospero left the island, he set Ariel free, to the great joy of that lively spirit who longed to wander uncontrolled, like a wild bird. His last command to Ariel was to watch over the ship in which they were all to set sail together, to calm the seas, and to send prospering winds.

Away flew Ariel to do this final task, singing his favorite song:

> *"Where the bee sucks, there suck I;*
> *In a cowslip's bell I lie;*
> *There I couch when owls do cry.*
> *On the bat's back I do fly*
> *After summer merrily.*
> *Merrily, merrily shall I live now*
> *Under the blossom that hangs on the bough."*

MYSTERY!
ADVENTURES
OF SHERLOCK HOLMES

THE RED-HEADED LEAGUE

by Sir Arthur Conan Doyle

1

I visited my friend, Mr. Sherlock Holmes, one day in the autumn of last year. I found him in deep conversation with a very stout, elderly gentleman with fiery red hair. I apologized for my intrusion and was about to leave, but Holmes abruptly pulled me into the room and closed the door behind me.

"You could not possibly have come at a better time, my dear Watson," he said. "I'd like you to meet Mr. Jabez Wilson." Sherlock Holmes turned to the red-haired man. "Dr. Watson has been my partner in many of my most successful cases, and I have no doubt that he will be a great help to me in yours also. Please, tell your story again."

The stout gentleman rose from his chair and gave a bob of greeting. He pulled a dirty, wrinkled newspaper from the inside pocket of his coat.

I took a good look at the man. I tried, just as Holmes would, to learn something about him from his dress or appearance.

I did not gain much from my inspection. Our visitor seemed an average British tradesman. There was nothing remarkable about the man except his blazing red head.

Sherlock Holmes noticed me eyeing our visitor, and he smiled at my questioning glance. "My dear Watson," he said, "beyond the obvious facts that he has at some time done manual labor, that he has been in China, that he has done much writing lately, I can deduce nothing else."

Mr. Jabez Wilson started in his chair. "How in the name of good fortune did you know all that, Mr. Holmes? How did you know I did manual labor? It's true, I began as a ship's carpenter."

"Your hands, my dear sir," said Holmes. "Your right hand is quite a size larger than your left. You have worked with it, and the muscles are more developed."

"Ah, of course, I forgot that. But the writing?"

"Your right cuff is very shiny for five inches, and the left has a smooth patch near the elbow where you rest it upon the desk."

"Well, yes," said Mr. Jabez Wilson. "But how did you know I've been to China?"

"The fish that you have tattooed above your right wrist could only have been done in China," said Holmes. "I have made a small study of tattoo marks and have even written a bit on the subject. The delicate pink of the fishes' scales is quite peculiar to China. In addition, I see a Chinese coin hanging from your watch chain. Now, Mr. Wilson, if you would tell us about your situation."

"Well, it is just as I have been telling you, Mr. Holmes," said Jabez Wilson, mopping his forehead. "I have a small business at Saxe-Coburg Square, near London. It's not very large, and lately it has only just given me a living. I used to be able to keep two assistants, but now I can only keep one. And it would be hard even to pay him, but he is willing to work for half wages, to learn the business."

"You seem most fortunate to have an employee willing to work for half wages," said Sherlock Holmes. "It is not a common experience these days. What is the name of this youth?"

"His name is Vincent Spaulding, and he's not such a youth, either. It's hard to say his age. I don't think I could find a smarter assistant, Mr. Holmes. I know very well that he could earn twice what I am able to give him. But if he is satisfied, why should I put ideas in his head?"

"Why, indeed? He is still with you, I presume?"

"Yes, sir. He and a girl who does a bit of cooking and cleaning. That's all I have in the house, for I am a widower and never had any family. We live very quietly, sir. But then, Spaulding, he came down into my office just this day eight weeks ago, with this very paper in his hand, and he says, 'Mr. Wilson, I wish that I was a red-headed man. Look at this.' And he handed me this paper. Here, read it for yourself."

I took the paper from him and read the following advertisement:

> *TO THE RED-HEADED LEAGUE: There is now a vacancy open which will pay a member of the League four pounds a week for light work. All red-headed men are eligible. Apply in person on Monday, at eleven o'clock, to Duncan Ross, at the offices of the League, 7 Pope's Court, Fleet Street.*

"What on earth does this mean?" I cried.

Holmes chuckled and wriggled in his chair, as was his habit when in high spirits. "It is a little off the beaten track, isn't it? Very good. Now, Mr. Wilson."

"Of course, my hair is red," Jabez Wilson began. "Spaulding thought that I might be chosen for the vacancy.

He even offered to come down with me. So we shut the business up, and started off for Fleet Street.

"I have never seen such a sight, Mr. Holmes. From north, south, east, and west every man who had a shade of red in his hair had tramped into the City to answer the advertisement. Fleet Street was choked with red-headed folk. Every shade of color they were—straw, lemon, orange, brick, Irish setter, liver, clay. But, as Spaulding said, there were not many who had my real, vivid, flame-colored tint.

"When I saw how many were waiting, I would have given up, but Spaulding would not hear of it. He pushed and pulled and butted until he got me through the crowd, and right up to the office steps. Two lines of people stood on the stairs, some going up in hope, and some coming back dejected. But we wedged in as well as we could, and soon found ourselves in the office.

"'This is Mr. Jabez Wilson,' Spaulding said to the manager, Duncan Ross, 'and he is willing to fill a vacancy in the League.'

"Mr. Ross, he gazed at my hair until I felt quite bashful. Then suddenly he plunged forward, shook my hand, and congratulated me warmly on my success. 'I cannot recall when I have seen anything so fine,' he said. Then Mr. Ross stepped over to the window and shouted through it at the top of his voice that the vacancy was filled. A groan of disappointment came up from below, and the folk all trooped away in different directions, until there was not a red head to be seen in the square.

"Mr. Ross told me that to earn the four pounds a week, I must stay in the office from ten to two every day, copying out the Encyclopedia Britannica. I thought it strange, but I agreed, and for eight weeks, I copied the books. Every morning I was there at ten, and every afternoon I left at two. And for eight weeks, I received four golden sovereigns for my work. But this morning, I went to the office, and found a sign on the door that said:

THE RED-HEADED LEAGUE IS DISSOLVED. Oct. 9, 1890.

"I went round to the offices, but no one had ever heard of the Red-Headed League or Mr. Duncan Ross. I did not wish to lose such a place without a struggle, and so," concluded Jabez Wilson, "as I had heard that you give advice to poor folk who need it, I came right away to you."

"And you did very wisely," said Holmes. "Your case is remarkable. I shall be happy to look into it. From what you have told me, I think graver problems hang from it than might at first sight appear. Tell me, what is he like, this assistant of yours who first called your attention to the advertisement, this Vincent Spaulding?"

"Small, stout-built, very quick in his ways, no hair on his face, around thirty years old. Has a white splash of acid on his forehead."

Holmes sat up in his chair. "I thought as much," said he. "Have you ever observed that his ears are pierced for earrings?"

"Yes, sir. He told me that a gypsy had done it for him when he was a lad."

"Hum!" said Holmes, sinking back, deep in thought. "And he has cared well for your business while you were away?"

"Nothing to complain of, sir. Though he does have his faults," said Mr. Wilson. "Never was such a fellow for photography. Snapping away with a camera when he ought to be learning, then diving down into the cellar like a rabbit into its hole to develop his pictures. That is his main fault; but, on the whole, he's a good worker."

Holmes nodded. "Mr. Wilson," he said, "today is Saturday. I hope that by Monday we will have solved your case."

"Well, Watson," said Holmes, when our visitor had left us, "let us go to Saxe-Coburg Square."

2

Holmes and I traveled by the Underground as far as Aldersgate, and a short walk took us to Saxe-Coburg Square. Four lines of dingy, two-storied brick houses looked out over a lawn of weedy grass. A brown board with *Jabez Wilson* in white letters announced the place where our red-headed client had his business. Sherlock Holmes stopped in front of it with his head to one side, and looked it all over, his eyes shining brightly. He thumped vigorously upon the pavement with his stick two or three times, then went up to the door and knocked. A bright-looking, clean-shaven young fellow opened it, and asked him to step in.

"Thank you," said Holmes, "I only wished to ask you how you would go from here to the Strand."

"Third right, fourth left," answered the assistant promptly, closing the door.

"Smart fellow, that," observed Holmes as we walked away. "I have known something of him before."

"Yes," said I, "Mr. Wilson's assistant seems to play a large part in this mystery of the Red-Headed League. I am sure that you knocked so that you might see him."

"Not him."

"What then?"

"The knees of his trousers."

"And what did you see?"

"What I expected to see."

"Why did you beat the pavement?"

"My dear doctor, this is a time for observation, not for talk. We are spies in an enemy's country. We know something of Saxe-Coburg Square. Let us now explore what lies behind it."

The road in which we found ourselves as we turned the corner was as different as the front of a painting is to the back. The street was one of the busiest in all of London.

"Let me see," said Holmes, standing at the corner, and glancing along the line, "I should like to remember the order of the houses here. There is Mortimer's, the tobacconist; the little newspaper stand, the Coburg branch of the City and Suburban Bank, the Vegetarian Restaurant, and McFarlane's carriage-building shop. That carries us right on to the next block. And now, doctor, we've done our work, so it's time we had some play—a sandwich, a cup of coffee, and then off to hear the violin at St. James Hall, where all is sweetness and harmony. You want to go home, no doubt."

"Yes, it would be as well."

"And I have some errands which will take some hours. This business at Saxe-Coburg Square is serious."

"Why serious?"

"A considerable crime is afoot. But I have every reason to believe that we shall be in time to stop it. I shall want your help tonight."

"At what time?"

"Ten will be early enough."

"I shall be at Baker Street at ten."

"Very well. And, I say, doctor! There may be some little danger, so kindly put your army revolver in your pocket." He waved his hand, turned on his heel, and disappeared in an instant among the crowd.

I trust that I am not a dense man. I had heard what Holmes had heard, and seen what he had seen. Yet he already knew what had happened and what was going to happen, while to me, the business was as mysterious as ever. I tried to puzzle it out, but gave up, and set the matter aside until night should bring an explanation.

3

It was a quarter-past nine when I started from home and made my way to Baker Street. On entering Holmes's room, I found him talking with two men, one of whom was Peter

Jones, the official police agent. The other was a long, thin, sad-faced man, with a very shiny hat.

"Ha! Our party is complete," said Holmes, buttoning up his pea-jacket, and taking his heavy hunting crop from the rack. "Watson, I think you know Mr. Jones, of Scotland Yard? Let me introduce you to Mr. Merryweather, who is to be our companion in tonight's adventure."

"I hope a wild goose may not prove to be the end of our chase," observed Mr. Merryweather gloomily.

"Mr. Merryweather," said Sherlock Holmes, "I think you will find the hunt worth your while tonight. I hope that I may have the pleasure of introducing you to John Clay, murderer and thief. Tonight he will try to steal no less than thirty thousand pounds from your bank. Now, gentlemen, it is past ten, and quite time that we started. If you two will take the first cab, Watson and I will follow in the second."

Sherlock Holmes said little during the long drive. As we rattled through the gas-lit streets, he lay back in the cab, humming the tunes he had heard in the afternoon.

"We are close now," my friend remarked. "This fellow Merryweather is a bank director, so he has a personal interest in the matter. And I thought it well to have Jones with us. He is incompetent, though he is brave as a bulldog and stubborn as a lobster if he gets his claws on anyone. Here we are, and they are waiting for us."

We had reached the street Holmes and I had visited in the morning. Mr. Merryweather unlocked the door to the City and Suburban bank. He led us down through endless tunnels and gates, until we came to the bank's cellar. We entered a huge vault, piled all round with crates and boxes.

"You are not very vulnerable from above," Holmes remarked, as he held up the lantern and gazed about him.

"Nor from below," said Mr. Merryweather, striking his stick upon the stones that lined the floor. "Why, dear me, it sounds quite hollow!" he remarked, looking up in surprise.

"I must really ask you to be a little more quiet!" said Holmes severely. "You might have just put our expedition in terrible danger. Might I ask that you sit on one of those boxes and not interfere?"

Mr. Merryweather perched upon a crate, with an injured expression on his face. Holmes fell upon his knees on the floor and, with the lantern and a magnifying glass, began to examine the cracks between the stones. After a few seconds, he sprang to his feet and put his glass in his pocket.

"We are at present, Doctor," he said, "in the cellar of the City branch of one of the main banks of London. The crate upon which Mr. Merryweather sits contains more than 2,000 gold pieces, not to mention these many other crates, all filled with gold. So you see, there are reasons why the more daring criminals of London should take an interest in this cellar. And I expect that within hours matters will come to a head. These are daring men, and they may do us some harm unless we are careful. I shall stand behind this crate. You conceal yourselves behind those. Then, when I flash a light upon them, close in swiftly."

We put out the lantern and took up our positions in the thick darkness of the vault. After waiting what seemed like hours, suddenly my eyes caught the glint of a light.

With a rending, tearing sound, one of the broad white stones in the floor turned over, and left a square, gaping hole, through which streamed the light of a lantern. A clean-cut, boyish face peeped out, looked around, then drew himself up out of the hole. He turned and began to haul out another man, nimble and small like himself, who had a pale face and a shock of very red hair.

"It's all clear," the first man whispered. "Have you the chisel and the bags? Great Scott! Jump, Archie, jump, and I'll swing for it!"

Sherlock Holmes had sprung out and seized the man by the collar. The other dived down the hole, and I heard the sound of tearing cloth as Jones clutched at his pant leg. The light flashed upon the barrel of a revolver, but Holmes's hunting crop came down on the man's wrist, and the pistol clinked upon the stone floor.

"It's no use, John Clay," said Holmes blandly. "You have no chance at all."

"So I see," the other answered coolly. "I fancy that my pal is all right, though I see you have got his coat-tails."

"Inspector Jones has three men waiting for him at the door," said Holmes.

"Oh, indeed? You seem to have thought of everything. I must compliment you."

"And I you," Holmes answered. "Your red-headed idea was very clever."

John Clay smiled. Then Jones clapped the handcuffs on him and led him away.

Later that night, Holmes explained. "You see, Watson, it was perfectly obvious to me that the Red-Headed League and copying the Encyclopedia were only a way to get Mr. Wilson out of his shop for several hours each day. The two rogues put the advertisement in the newspaper. One lures Mr. Wilson to the League, the other pretends to be the manager. From Mr. Wilson's description, I knew the assistant was one of the most daring criminals in London."

"But how could you guess what the men wanted?"

"The man's business was a small one, so they could not want to steal from him. It must then be something out of the house, but what? I thought of the assistant's fondness for photography, and his trick of vanishing into the cellar. The cellar! He was doing something in the cellar—something which took many hours a day for months on end. I could think of nothing except that he was digging a tunnel to some other building.

"When we visited the square, I beat upon the pavement with my stick to see if the cellar stretched out in front of the building or behind. It was not in front. When I rang the bell, I saw that the assistant's pant-knees were worn and stained, from hours of digging. When we walked round the corner, I saw that the bank was behind Mr. Wilson's shop, and I knew

I had solved the problem. I called Scotland Yard and Mr. Merryweather, and the rest you saw yourself."

"But how did you know that they would make their attempt tonight?" I asked.

"Well, when they closed the League office, that was a sign that they cared no longer about Mr. Jabez Wilson's presence. In other words, they had completed their tunnel. But they had to use it soon, or it might be discovered. Saturday would suit them better than any other day, as it would give them two days before the bank opened and anyone noticed the money was missing."

"You reasoned it out beautifully," I exclaimed, admiringly. "It is so long a chain, and yet every link rings true."

"It saved me from boredom," he answered, yawning.

The Adventure of the Blue Carbuncle

by Sir Arthur Conan Doyle

1

I called upon my friend, Sherlock Holmes, on the second morning after Christmas, to wish him a happy holiday. He was lounging upon the sofa in a purple dressing gown among a pile of crumpled morning newspapers. He was peering through a magnifying glass at an old, shabby black hat, cracked in several places.

"Am I interrupting you?" I asked.

"Not at all. I am glad to have a friend with whom I can discuss my findings."

I sat down in his armchair and warmed my hands before his crackling fire. A sharp frost had set in, and the windows were thick with the ice crystals. "I suppose," I remarked, "that, homely as it looks, that hat has some deadly story linked on to it. Is it the clue that will guide you to the solution of a mystery, or the punishment of a crime?"

"No, no. No crime," said Sherlock Holmes, laughing. "Only one of those odd little events that happen when you have four million people crowded together within the space of a few square miles. You know Peterson, the commissionaire?"

"Yes."

"This trophy belongs to him."

"Oh, it is his hat?"

"No, no, he found it. No one knows who the owner is. Watson, don't look at it as just a battered billycock. Instead, see it as an interesting problem.

"Peterson brought it here on Christmas morning, along with a good fat goose. The facts are these: about four o'clock on Christmas morning, Peterson, a very honest fellow, was coming home from a holiday party. In front of him, he saw a tall man, carrying a white goose over his shoulder. As the man reached the corner of Goodge Street, a group of roughs attacked him. One knocked off his hat. So the man raised his stick to defend himself. But when he swung the stick over his head, he accidentally smashed the shop window behind him.

"Peterson had rushed forward to protect the stranger from his attackers. But the man, shocked at having broken the window, and seeing an official-looking person in uniform running towards him, dropped his goose and took to his heels. The roughs also ran away. And so Peterson was left with this battered hat and a marvelous Christmas goose."

"Which Peterson surely returned to the man?" I asked.

"My dear fellow, there lies the problem. 'For Mrs. Henry Baker' was printed upon a small card which was tied to the bird's left leg. You can see the initials 'H. B.' upon the lining of this hat. But there are hundreds of Henry Bakers in this city of ours. It will not be easy to return the hat and the goose to the right man."

"What, then, did Peterson do?"

"Peterson knows that even the smallest problems interest me, so he brought me the goose and the hat. The goose had to be eaten before it spoiled, so he took it home. I, of course, have the man's hat. And I would like to return it to him, along with his Christmas dinner."

"How on earth will you figure out who he is? Not from his hat!"

"Precisely so."

"But you are joking. What can you gather from this old battered felt?"

"Here is my magnifying glass. You know my methods. What can you find out yourself about the man who has worn this hat?"

I took the tattered object in my hands and turned it over. It was a very ordinary black hat of the usual round shape, though much the worse for wear. The lining had been of red silk, but was now spotted and stained. There was no maker's name, but, as Holmes had remarked, the initials "H. B." were written on one side. For the rest, it was cracked, very dusty, and worn in several places, though it appeared that the owner had smeared the worn patches with ink to hide them.

"I can see nothing," said I, handing it back to my friend.

"On the contrary, Watson, you can see everything, but you fail to reason from what you see. You are too timid in drawing your inferences."

"Please tell me, what can you infer from this hat?"

Holmes picked up the hat and gazed at it. "Obviously, this man was fairly well-to-do within the last three years. But he has now fallen upon hard times. That may be why his wife is angry with him."

"My dear Holmes!"

"Still, he cares what people think of him. He mostly stays at home, and he is out of shape. He has grizzled hair, which he has had cut within the last few days, and which he smoothes with lime-cream."

"You are certainly joking, Holmes."

"Not in the least. Is it possible that you do not see how I reached these conclusions?"

"I must confess that I am unable to follow you."

"This hat is three years old. These flat brims curled at the edge were fashionable then. It is a hat of the very best quality. If this man could afford to buy such an expensive hat three years ago, and has had no new hat since, then he has certainly gone down in the world."

"Well, that is clear enough," I said. "But what about the rest: that he stays at home, is out of shape, has grizzled hair that has been recently cut, and that he uses lime-cream?"

"All of that you can see when you look through a magnifying glass. Look, there are a number of hair-ends, clean cut by a barber's scissors. They're quite sticky, and the whole hat smells of lime-cream. This dust is not the gritty, gray dust of the street but the fluffy brown dust of the house, showing that it has been hung up indoors most of the time. The marks of moisture upon the inside are proof positive that the wearer perspires a lot while walking, so he is probably not in good shape."

"But his wife—you said that she was angry with him."

"This hat has not been brushed for weeks. My dear Watson, when you have a week's worth of dust upon your hat, and when your wife allows you to go out that way, I will fear that you also will have made her quite upset."

"But he might be a bachelor."

"No, remember the card on the bird's leg, which said 'For Mrs. Henry Baker.' He was bringing home the goose as a peace offering to his wife."

"You're very clever," said I, laughing. "But no crime has been committed. No harm has been done except the loss of a goose and an old hat. All of this seems to be rather a waste of energy."

As Sherlock Holmes opened his mouth to reply, the door flew open, and Peterson, the commissionaire, rushed into the apartment. His cheeks were flushed and he was dazed with astonishment.

"The goose, Mr. Holmes! The goose!" he gasped.

"What of it? By the looks of you, it must have gotten up from its platter and flapped off through the window."

"No, see here, sir! See what my wife found in its crop!" Peterson opened his hand and showed a sparkling blue stone. It was smaller than a bean, but so brilliant that it twinkled like a star in the dark hollow of his hand.

Sherlock Holmes sat up with a whistle. "Peterson, that is a treasure indeed. Do you know what you have there?"

"A diamond, sir? A precious stone?"

"It's more than *a* precious stone. It is *the* precious stone."

"Not the Countess of Morcar's blue carbuncle!" I cried.

"Precisely so," said Holmes.

"It was stolen just a few days ago, wasn't it?" I asked.

"Precisely so, on December 22nd, just five days ago," replied Holmes. "John Horner, a plumber, was accused of

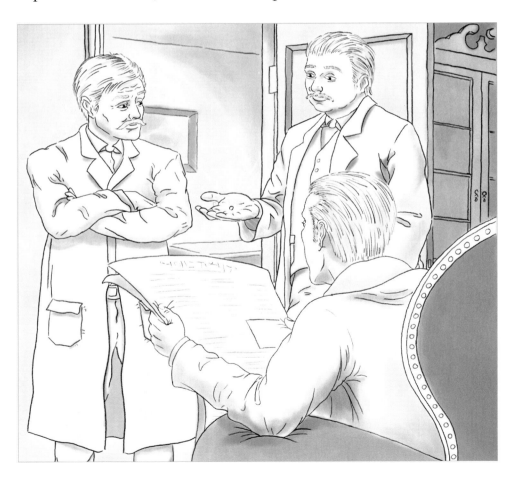

having stolen it from the Countess's jewel-case. I have some articles about it here, I believe." Holmes rummaged among his newspapers. At last, he smoothed one out and read:

HOTEL COSMOPOLITAN JEWEL ROBBERY

John Horner, 26, plumber, was arrested on the charge of having stolen from the Countess of Morcar the valuable gem known as the blue carbuncle.

James Ryder, head attendant at the hotel, said that he had shown Horner to the Countess's dressing room on the day of the robbery to fix a pipe. He stayed with Horner for a while, but then was called away.

When Ryder returned, he found that Horner had disappeared and that the bureau had been forced open. Also, a small case in which the Countess kept her jewel was lying empty upon the dressing table.

Ryder called the police. Horner was arrested that evening, but the stone was not found on him or at his home. The arresting officer reported that Horner struggled frantically and strongly declared his innocence.

At the court hearing, evidence was given that the prisoner had been previously convicted of robbery. Horner, who was greatly upset, fainted away and was carried out of court.

"Hum! So much for the police," said Holmes thoughtfully. "The question for us is, how did the Countess's blue carbuncle travel from her jewelry-case to Mr. Henry Baker's Christmas goose? Let us try the simplest way first. We will advertise in the evening newspapers. If this fails, we will have to try another method. Please pass me a pencil and that slip of paper, Watson. Now, then:

Found at the corner of Goodge Street, a goose and a
black felt hat. Mr. Henry Baker can have them by
coming to 221B Baker Street at 6:30 this evening.

"That is very clear," I said. "But will Mr. Baker see it?"

"Well, he is sure to keep an eye on the papers, since, to a poor man, the loss was a heavy one. Everyone to whom he told the story will see his name in the ad and show it to him. Here you are, Peterson, run down to the newspapers and have this ad put in tonight."

"Very well, sir. And the stone?"

"Ah, yes, I will keep the stone. Thank you. And, I say, Peterson, please buy a goose on your way back and leave it here with me. We must have one to give to this gentleman in place of the one your family is now enjoying."

After Peterson left, Holmes took up the stone and held it against the light. "It's a pretty thing," said he. "See how it glitters and sparkles. Of course it is a magnet for crime. This tiny piece of crystallized charcoal has already been the object of several robberies and murders. Who would think that so pretty a toy would send men to prison? I'll lock it up in my strong-box and send a message to the Countess to say that we have it."

"Holmes," I asked, "do you think that the plumber, Horner, is innocent?"

"I'm not sure."

"Well, then, do you think Henry Baker had anything to do with the crime?"

"I think Henry Baker is absolutely innocent. He probably has no idea that the bird he carried was more valuable than a goose made of solid gold. But I will know that when the man answers the advertisement."

"And you can do nothing until then?"

"Nothing."

"In that case I shall return to my patients. But I shall come back at 6:30. For I should like to see the solution to this tangled case."

"Very glad to see you. I dine at seven. There is a turkey, I believe. But before she starts cooking, perhaps I ought to ask Mrs. Hudson to examine the bird's crop."

2

It was a little after half-past six when I returned to Baker Street. As I neared the house, I saw a tall man waiting outside Holmes's door. Just as I arrived the door was opened, and we were shown up together to Holmes's rooms.

"Mr. Henry Baker, I believe," said Holmes, rising from his armchair. "Please take this seat by the fire. It is a cold night. Ah, Watson, you have just come at the right time. Now, Mr. Baker, is this your hat?"

"Yes, sir, it certainly is." Henry Baker ran his hand through his grizzled hair. I noticed the scent of lime-cream.

"We kept these things for some days," said Holmes, "because we expected to see an advertisement from you giving your address. Why didn't you advertise?"

Our visitor laughed sheepishly. "Shillings are not so plentiful with me as they once were. I thought that the gang of roughs who attacked me had carried off both my hat and the bird. I thought it would be a waste of money to try to get them back."

"Of course. By the way, about the bird, we had to eat it."

"To eat it!" Our visitor half rose from his chair in his excitement.

"Yes, it would have spoiled if we hadn't. But here is another goose. It is about the same weight and perfectly fresh. Will it do?"

"Oh, certainly, certainly," answered Mr. Baker, sighing with relief.

"Of course, we still have the feathers, legs, crop, and so on of your own bird, so if you wish—"

The man burst into a hearty laugh. "They might be useful as souvenirs of my adventure," he said, "but beyond that, they are of no use to me."

Sherlock Holmes glanced sharply at me with a slight shrug of his shoulders.

"There is your hat, then, and there is your bird," he said. "By the way, would you tell me where you got the other one? I have never seen a better goose."

"Certainly, sir," said Baker, tucking the goose under his arm. "I bought it from a man named Windigate at the Alpha Inn." He clapped his hat upon his head, thanked us, and went off upon his way.

"So much for Mr. Henry Baker," said Holmes when he had closed the door behind him. "He knows nothing about the jewel. But would you like to follow up on his clue while it is still hot?"

"By all means," I replied.

We trudged through the snow to the Alpha Inn. Holmes walked to the bar and ordered two glasses of ale from the ruddy-faced, white-aproned landlord.

"Your ale should be excellent if it is as good as your geese," said he.

"My geese?" The man seemed surprised.

"Yes. I just spoke to Mr. Henry Baker. He said he'd bought his goose from you."

"Ah! Yes, I see. Sorry, sir, but them's not our geese."

"Indeed! Whose are they, then?"

"Well, I got the two dozen from a salesman in Covent Garden."

"Indeed? I know some of them. Who was it?"

"Breckinridge is his name."

"Ah! I don't know him. Well, here's to your good health, landlord, and prosperity to your house. Good-night."

As we came out into the frosty air, Holmes buttoned his coat and said, "Now for Mr. Breckinridge. Remember, Watson, even though we have only a goose at this end of the chain, at the other end, there is a man who will spend years in prison unless we can prove that he is innocent."

3

Holmes and I hurried to Covent Garden Market. One of the largest stalls had the name *Breckinridge* written on it. The salesman was helping a boy put up the shutters.

"Good-evening. Sold out of geese, I see," said Holmes, pointing at the bare slabs of marble. "Fine birds they were, too. Where did you get them from?"

To my surprise, the salesman was suddenly furious.

"Now, then, mister, what do you want? Let's have it straight, now."

"It's straight enough. I want to know who sold you your geese."

"Well then, I won't tell you. So now!"

"Oh, it's not important. But why are you so upset over such a small thing?"

"Upset? You'd be upset, too, if you were as pestered as I am. When I pay good money for a good goose, that should be the end of the business. But all day long, it's been 'Where are the geese?' and 'Who did you sell the geese to?' and 'What will you take for the geese?' You'd think they were the only geese in the world, to hear the fuss that's been made over them."

"Well, I don't know who else has been asking," said Holmes casually. "If you won't tell us, the bet is off, that's all. But I'm always ready to back my opinion on a matter of geese, and I have a fiver on it that the bird I ate is country bred."

"Well, then, you've lost your fiver, for it's town bred," snapped the salesman.

"It's nothing of the kind."

"I say it is."

"I don't believe it."

"D'you think you know more about geese than I, who have handled them ever since I was a nipper? I tell you, those birds were town bred."

"You'll never persuade me to believe that."

"Will you bet, then?" asked the salesman.

"It would be taking your money, because I know I'm right. But I'll bet a sovereign, just to teach you not to be so obstinate."

The salesman snorted. "Bring me the book, Bill," he said.

The boy brought out a great, greasy volume. He laid it beneath the lamp.

"Now then, Mr. Know-It-All," said the salesman, "You see this book?"

"Well?"

"That's the list of the folk from whom I buy. D'you see? Well, then, here on this page are the country folk I buy from. Now, then! You see this other page in red ink? Well, that is a list of my town suppliers. Now, look at that third name. Just read it out to me."

"Mrs. Oakshott, 117 Brixton Road—egg and poultry supplier," read Holmes.

"Quite so. Now, read the last entry."

"'December 22nd. Twenty-four geese at 7 shillings.'"

"Quite so. There you are. And underneath?"

"'Sold to Mr. Windigate of the Alpha Inn, at 12 shillings.'"

"What have you to say now, Mr. Know-It-All?"

Sherlock Holmes drew a sovereign from his pocket and threw it down upon the slab. He turned away as though he was disgusted. But a few yards off, he stopped under a lamppost and laughed in his hearty, silent way.

"When you see a man with a horse-racing form sticking out of his pocket, you can always get him to talk with a bet," said he, chuckling.

Just then, a loud hubbub broke out from the stall that we had just left. Turning round we saw Breckinridge shaking his fist at a little rat-faced fellow.

"I've had enough of you and your geese!" Breckinridge shouted. "If you come pestering me again, I'll set the dog at you!"

"Ha! This may save us a visit to Brixton Road," whispered Holmes. "Come with me. Let's see who this fellow is." Holmes strode through the crowd, and touched the little man on the shoulder. The man jumped and turned around, his face pale.

"You will excuse me," said Holmes blandly, "but I could not help overhearing your conversation with the salesman. Perhaps I can help you."

"Who are you?" asked the man in a quavering voice. "How could you know anything of the matter?"

"My name is Sherlock Holmes. It is my business to know what other people don't know."

"But you can know nothing of this!"

"Excuse me, I know everything about it. You are trying to trace a goose sold by Mrs. Oakshott, of Brixton Road, to a salesman named Breckinridge, by him in turn to Mr. Windigate, of the Alpha, and by him to Mr. Henry Baker."

"Oh, sir, you're just the man I am looking for!" cried the little fellow, almost in tears.

"Of course. But please tell me who it is that I have the pleasure of helping."

The man paused for a moment. "My name is John Robinson," he answered with a sly glance.

"No, your real name," said Holmes sweetly. "It is always awkward doing business with a false one."

The stranger blushed. "Well then," said he, "my real name is James Ryder."

Sherlock Holmes hailed a cab. "Precisely so—the head attendant at the Hotel Cosmopolitan. Please step into the cab, and I shall soon be able to tell you everything you wish to know."

4

In a half-hour we were back at Baker Street.

"Here we are!" said Holmes cheerily as we filed into his rooms. "Now, then! You want to know what became of a white goose with a black bar across the tail?"

Ryder trembled. "Oh, sir," he cried, "can you tell me where it went to?"

"It came here."

"Here?"

"Yes, and it was a most amazing bird. I'm not surprised that you want to find it. You know, it laid an egg after it was dead—the prettiest, brightest little blue egg ever seen."

Holmes unlocked his strong-box and held up the blue carbuncle, which shone out like a star. Ryder's eyes bulged with fear.

"The game's up, Ryder," said Holmes quietly. "You had heard of the Countess's blue carbuncle, had you not?"

"Her maid told me about it," Ryder said in a crackling voice.

"I see. Well, the temptation of sudden wealth was too much for you. But you were not very careful in the means you used. You knew that this man Horner, the plumber, had been convicted of robbery before. So, you damaged the pipes in the Countess's room, then sent for Horner. When the gem was stolen, you knew that everyone would suspect him. After he left, you cracked open the jewel-case, raised the alarm, and had the poor man arrested."

Ryder threw himself down on the rug and clutched at Holmes's knees. "Have mercy!" he shrieked. "Think of my parents! It would break their hearts. I never went wrong before! I never will again. I swear it. I'll swear it on a Bible. Oh, don't bring it into court! Please!"

"Get back into your chair!" said Holmes sternly. "It is very well to cringe and crawl now. But you thought little enough of this poor Horner being punished for a crime he did not commit."

"I will go away, Mr. Holmes. I will leave the country. Then the charge against him will break down."

"Hum! We will talk about that. Now let us hear the true story of how the stone got into the goose and how the goose got to market. Tell us the truth, for that is your only hope of safety."

"I will tell you what happened, sir," said he. "When Horner was arrested, I knew I had to get away with the stone at once. I did not know if the police would search me and my room, too. The hotel wasn't safe, so I went to my sister's house. She and her husband, a man named Oakshott, raise geese for market."

Ryder passed his tongue over his parched lips and then continued. "I have a friend who was once a thief. I knew that if I took the stone to him, he would show me how to sell the stone for money. But the police could stop me and search me at any time. How could I keep the jewel safe?

"I remembered that my sister told me I might have my pick of her geese for a Christmas present. So I went into the goose yard, and caught a big white bird with a barred tail. I pried its bill open and thrust the stone into its throat. The bird gulped, and I felt the stone pass into its crop. Then it broke loose and fluttered off among the others.

"I told my sister which goose I wanted. She said I could take it with me. So I caught it and took it to my friend. But when we cut open the goose, my heart turned to water. There was no sign of the stone.

"I rushed back to my sister's and hurried into the yard. But there was not a bird to be seen. She told me they had all gone to Breckinridge at Covent Garden. I asked her if there was another with a barred tail. She said yes, and that they were so alike she herself couldn't tell them apart.

"Well, I ran to this man Breckinridge, but he'd sold them all. You know the rest. My sister thinks that I am going mad. If only she knew! I think I might be. Now I am myself a thief, and I never even touched the wealth for which I sold my character." He burst into sobs, and buried his face in his hands.

There was a long silence, broken only by Sherlock Holmes tapping his fingertips on the table. Suddenly, my friend rose and threw open the door.

"Get out!" he said.

"What, sir? Oh, Heaven bless you!"

"No more words. Get out!"

No more words were needed. There was a rush, a clatter upon the stairs, the bang of a door, and the crisp rattle of running footfalls from the street.

"After all, Watson," said Holmes, "Horner is not in danger. Ryder will not speak against him, and the stone will be returned, so the case will fall apart. Perhaps I am committing a crime, but perhaps I am saving a soul. This fellow will not go wrong again. He is too frightened. If we send him to jail now, we will make him a jail-bird for life."

He reached for his clay pipe. "Besides," he concluded, "it is the season of forgiveness. Chance sent us a most entertaining problem, and solving it has been its own reward. Now, Doctor, if you will join me, we will begin another investigation, in which also a bird will be the most delicious object."

THE REAL SHERLOCK HOLMES
by Irving Wallace

Sherlock Holmes was one of the first of all the storybook detectives, and he is still the greatest. He is perhaps known to more people than any other character in fiction. You must have seen pictures of him—a powerful man of six feet two, dressed in a cape and deerstalker hat, with a pipe in his mouth and a magnifying glass in his hand.

Yet it was not his appearance that made Sherlock Holmes famous, but his marvelous powers of detection. In "The Adventure of the Norwood Builder," a popular Sherlock Holmes story, a young man rushes into Holmes's sitting room at 221B Baker Street, London. "I am John McFarlane," he says, panting heavily.

Sherlock Holmes lazily replies, "You mentioned your name as if I should recognize it. I assure you that beyond the obvious facts that you are a bachelor, a lawyer, a Freemason and an asthmatic, I know nothing whatever about you."

Of course, Holmes was doing no more than using his eyes cleverly. He noticed that the visitor's clothes needed repairing—a sign that he was not married. A legal form sticking out of the man's pocket told Holmes that he was a lawyer. From his watch chain hung a charm worn only by members of the Society of Freemasons. He was also panting in a way that suggested he had asthma.

John McFarlane was in serious trouble. He was suspected of having murdered a builder in Norwood. In fact, the builder hadn't been murdered at all. For reasons of revenge, he had staged his own "murder," leaving evidence to show that McFarlane had killed him and destroyed the body in a fire. Holmes solved the case brilliantly, and the wicked builder was soon discovered, hiding in a secret passage in his house.

When you read how Holmes can tell so much about someone he has only just met, you may wonder if such a thing is possible. "It's all very well in a book," you may say, "but no one could do that in real life." Well, there was someone who did it in real life. He was a well-known surgeon in Edinburgh, and his name was Dr. Joseph Bell.

For fifty years Dr. Bell taught at Edinburgh University. He used to tell his pupils that if they were to become good doctors they must first learn to use their eyes properly.

"Most people see," he said, "but they do not observe. Look at a man, and in his face you will find clues to where he comes from. His hands will show you what work he does. The rest of the story is told by the clothes—even by a piece of lint sticking to his coat."

He would glance at some stranger, then remark, "A cobbler, I see." Later he would point out to the students that a cobbler's trousers were always worn smooth on the inside of the knee, for that was where he held the shoe he was repairing.

One of Dr. Bell's pupils was a young man called Arthur Conan Doyle. He graduated from the university in 1881, and for six years struggled to make a living as a doctor. At last he found himself so short of money that, in desperation, he turned to writing. He decided to try a detective story.

Wanting a new kind of detective for his book, Conan Doyle thought of his old teacher, Dr. Bell. If the surgeon had been a detective, he would surely have treated detection as a science, instead of the romantic game it was at that time. So Conan Doyle invented his scientific detective, Sherlock Holmes. But Holmes's brilliant methods are really those of Dr. Bell.

Dr. Bell's Methods

One afternoon Dr. Bell was at his desk in the hospital when somebody knocked at the door.

"Come in," called the surgeon. A man entered. Dr. Bell stared at him. "Why are you worried?"

"How do you know I am worried?"

"The four knocks. Those who have no cares in the world only bother to knock twice or, at the most, three times."

It turned out that the man was worried.

On another occasion, when Conan Doyle was acting as Dr. Bell's assistant, a patient entered the room.

"Did you enjoy your walk over the golf links today, as you came in from the south side of town?" Dr. Bell asked.

"Why, yes, did you see me?" said the patient.

Dr. Bell said he had not seen him. "But," he explained, "on a showery day, the reddish clay of the golf course sticks to the shoes. There is no clay like that anywhere else."

The Case of the Retired Sergeant

Sherlock Holmes not only follows Dr. Bell's methods. There are times when he actually uses bits of his detective work. When people came into his consulting room, Dr. Bell would tell them what was wrong with them before they had time to open their mouths. He would even give them details of their past lives, and he hardly ever made a mistake.

One day, as a new patient entered, Dr. Bell studied him carefully and said, "Well, you've served in the Army, in a Scottish regiment, and you have only just retired."

"Aye, sir," said the man.

"You were a sergeant, and you were stationed in Barbados."

"Aye, sir."

Dr. Bell turned to his students. "You see, gentlemen, he is a polite man, but he did not remove his hat when he came into the room. They do not do so in the Army. But if he had been out of the Army for long, he would have learned civilian habits. Clearly he is used to giving orders, as a sergeant would. He is obviously Scottish, so he was probably in a Scottish regiment. As to Barbados, he is suffering from a disease that is common in the West Indies."

There is an incident almost the same as this one in the Sherlock Holmes story "The Greek Interpreter."

Sherlock Holmes soon became very popular, as he still is today. He seems like a real detective, because he always tells you exactly how he solves each crime. In a way, of course, he was real, and perhaps that is why he appears so lifelike.

Dr. Bell, the original Sherlock Holmes, once caught a man out beautifully. He was teaching some students when a patient walked into the room.

"Gentlemen," said Dr. Bell, "this man has been a soldier in a Highland regiment. He probably played in the band."

The surgeon pointed out that when the patient walked he swaggered a little, like a Highland piper. But the man quickly said that he was a shoemaker, and that he had never even been in the Army.

The surgeon then asked him to remove his shirt. He did so, and the students saw a little blue D branded on his chest. Dr. Bell explained that soldiers who deserted from the Army in the Crimean War were branded with a D when they were caught.

The man finally confessed that he had once played in the band of a Highland regiment. Dr. Bell turned to his audience, and used the words Sherlock Holmes was to make famous: "It was really elementary, gentlemen."

Anyone Can Be a Detective

Dr. Bell believed it was vital for doctors and detectives to use their eyes intelligently. He also said that anyone who found his life dull could change it into one of excitement and adventure, just by practicing his powers of observation.

His sister once described how he made train journeys more exciting. "When the family traveled by train, he would tell us where the other passengers came from, where they were going, and even something about their jobs. Then he would ask them whether he was right or not. He was right so often that we thought him a magician."

However, Dr. Bell would show that his detective feats were not due to magic, but to good observation.

"The work that a man does leaves its mark on his hands," he used to say. "The scars of a coal miner are quite different from those of a man who works in a quarry. The hands of both the carpenter and the stonemason grow hard, but not in the same way."

Yet even Dr. Bell sometimes made mistakes. Luckily, he also had a sense of humor. When people asked him to give examples of his skill as a detective, he liked to tell this story:

One day he and his pupils were examining a patient in a hospital bed. "Aren't you a musician?" Dr. Bell asked him.

"Aye," admitted the sick man.

"You see, gentlemen, it is quite simple. This man has a disease of the cheek muscles, from too much blowing on wind instruments. We need only to ask him, and he will admit it. What musical instrument do you play, my man?"

The man got up on his elbows. "The big drum, doctor!"

Favorites from Famous Books: Little Women

from
LITTLE WOMEN
by Louisa May Alcott

A LETTER

"Christmas won't be Christmas without any presents," grumbled Jo, lying on the rug.

"It's so dreadful to be poor!" sighed Meg, looking down at her old dress.

"I don't think it's fair for some girls to have plenty of pretty things, and other girls nothing at all," added little Amy, with an injured sniff.

"We've got Father and Mother and each other," said Beth contentedly from her corner.

The four young faces on which the firelight shone brightened at the cheerful words, but darkened again as Jo said sadly, "We haven't got Father, and shall not have him for a long time." She didn't say "perhaps never," but each silently added it, thinking of Father far away, where the fighting was.

Nobody spoke for a minute. Then Meg said in an altered tone, "You know the reason Mother proposed not having any Christmas presents this year was because it is going to be a hard winter for everyone. She thinks we ought not to spend money for pleasure, when our men are suffering so in the army. We can't do much, but we can make our little sacrifices, and ought to do it gladly. But I am afraid I don't." And Meg shook her head, as she thought regretfully of all the pretty things she wanted.

"But I don't think the little we should spend would do any good. We've each got a dollar, and the army wouldn't be much helped by our giving that. I agree not to accept anything from Mother or you, but I do want to buy *Undine and Sintram* for myself. I've wanted it for so long," said Jo, who was a bookworm.

"I've planned to spend mine on new music," said Beth, with a little sigh.

"I shall get a nice box of Faber's drawing pencils. I really need them," said Amy decidedly.

"Mother didn't say anything about our money, and she won't wish us to give up everything. Let's each buy what we want and have a little fun. I'm sure we work hard enough to earn it," cried Jo.

"I know *I* do—teaching those tiresome children nearly all day, when I'm longing to enjoy myself at home," began Meg, in the complaining tone again.

"You don't have half such a hard time as I do," said Jo. "How would you like to be shut up for hours with Aunt March? She's never satisfied, and worries till you're ready to fly out the window or cry."

"It's naughty to fret, but I do think washing dishes and keeping things tidy is the worst thing in the world. It makes me cross, and my hands get so stiff, I can't practice well at all." And Beth looked at her rough hands with a sigh.

"I don't believe any of you suffer as I do," cried Amy, "for you don't have to go to school with impertinent girls, who plague you if you don't know your lessons, and laugh at your dresses, and label your father if he isn't rich, and insult you when your nose isn't nice."

"If you mean *libel*, I'd say so, and not talk about labels, as if Papa was a pickle bottle," advised Jo, laughing.

"I know what I mean, and you needn't be *statirical* about it. It's proper to use good words, and improve your *vocabilary*," returned Amy, with dignity.

"Don't peck at one another, children. Don't you wish we had the money Papa lost when we were little, Jo? Dear me! How happy and good we'd be, if we had no worries!" said Meg, who could remember better times.

"You said the other day you thought we were happier than the King children, for they were fighting and fretting all the time, in spite of their money."

"So I did, Beth. Well, I think we are. Though we do have to work, we make fun for ourselves, and are a pretty jolly set, as Jo would say."

"Jo does use such slang words!" observed Amy, with a reproving look at the long figure stretched out on the rug. Jo immediately sat up, put her hands in her pockets, and began to whistle.

"Don't, Jo, it's so boyish!"

"That's why I do it."

"I detest rude, unladylike girls!"

"I hate affected, niminy-piminy chits!"

"'Birds in their little nests agree,'" sang Beth, the peacemaker, with such a funny look on her face that both sharp voices softened to a laugh, and the "pecking" ended for that time.

"Really, girls, you are both to blame," said Meg, beginning to lecture in her elder-sisterly fashion. "You are old enough to leave off such boyish tricks, and to behave better, Josephine. It didn't matter so much when you were a little girl. But now you are so tall, and turn up your hair, you should remember that you are a young lady!"

"I'm not! And if turning up my hair makes me one, I'll wear it in two tails till I'm twenty," cried Jo, shaking down her chestnut mane. "I hate to think I've got to grow up, and be Miss March, and wear long gowns! It's bad enough to be a girl, anyway, when I like boys' games and work and manners! I can't get over my disappointment in not being a boy, and it's worse than ever now, for I'm dying to go and fight with Papa, and I can only stay at home and knit, like a poky old woman!"

"Poor Jo! It's too bad, but it can't be helped. So you must try to be contented by making your name boyish, and playing brother to us girls," said Beth, stroking the rough head at her knee with a hand that all the dishwashing and dusting in the world could not make ungentle at its touch.

"As for you, Amy," continued Meg, "you are altogether too particular and prim. Your airs are funny now, but you'll grow up an affected little goose, if you don't take care. I like your nice manners and refined ways of speaking, when you don't try to be elegant. But your absurd words are as bad as Jo's slang."

"If Jo is a tomboy and Amy a goose, what am I, please?" asked Beth, ready to share the lecture.

"You're a dear, and nothing else," answered Meg warmly. And no one contradicted her, for the "Mouse" was the pet of the family.

The clock struck six and, having swept up the hearth, Beth put a pair of slippers down to warm. Somehow the sight of the old shoes had a good effect upon the girls, for their mother was coming, and everyone brightened to welcome her. Meg stopped lecturing and lighted the lamp, Amy got out of the easy chair without being asked, and Jo forgot how tired she was as she sat up to hold the slippers nearer to the blaze.

"They are quite worn out. Marmee must have a new pair."

"I thought I'd get her some with my dollar," said Beth.

"No, I shall!" cried Amy.

"I'm the oldest," began Meg.

But Jo cut in with a decided, "I'm the man of the family now Papa is away, and I shall provide the slippers, for he told me to take special care of Mother while he was gone."

"I'll tell you what we'll do," said Beth. "Let's each get her something for Christmas, and not get anything for ourselves."

"That's like you, dear! What will we get?" exclaimed Jo.

Everyone thought soberly for a minute, then Meg announced, as if the idea was suggested by the sight of her own pretty hands, "I shall give her a nice pair of gloves."

"Army shoes, best to be had," cried Jo.

"Some handkerchiefs, all hemmed," said Beth.

"I'll get a little bottle of cologne. She likes it, and it won't cost much, so I'll have some left to buy my pencils," added Amy.

"Glad to find you so merry, my girls," said a cheery voice at the door. The girls turned to welcome a tall motherly lady with a "can-I-help-you" look about her. She was not elegantly dressed, but a noble-looking woman, and the girls thought the gray cloak and the unfashionable bonnet covered the most splendid mother in the world.

"Well, dearies, how have you got on today? There was so much to do, getting the boxes ready to go tomorrow, that I didn't come home to dinner. Has anyone called, Beth? How is your cold, Meg? Jo, you look tired to death. Come and kiss me, my baby Amy."

While making these maternal inquiries Mrs. March got her wet things off, her warm slippers on, and sitting down in the easy chair, drew Amy to her lap, preparing to enjoy the happiest hour of her busy day. The girls flew about, trying to make things comfortable, each in her own way. Meg arranged the tea-table. Jo brought wood and set chairs, dropping, overturning, and clattering everything she touched. Beth trotted to and fro between parlor and kitchen, quiet and busy, while Amy gave directions to everyone, as she sat with her hands folded.

As they gathered around the table, Mrs. March said, with a particularly happy face, "I've got a treat for you."

A quick, bright smile went round like a streak of sunshine. Beth clapped her hands, regardless of the biscuit she held, and Jo tossed up her napkin, crying, "A letter! A letter!"

"Yes, a nice long letter. He is well, and he thinks he shall get through the cold season better than we feared. He sends all sorts of loving wishes for Christmas, and an especial message to you girls," said Mrs. March, patting her pocket as if she had got a treasure there.

"I think it was so splendid of Father to go as a chaplain when he was too old to be drafted, and not strong enough for a soldier," said Meg warmly.

"Don't I wish I could go as a drummer? Or a nurse, so I could be near to him and help him," exclaimed Jo.

"It must be very disagreeable to sleep in a tent, and eat all sorts of bad tasting things, and drink out of a tin mug," sighed Amy.

"When will he come home, Marmee?" asked Beth, with a little quiver in her voice.

"Not for many months, dear, unless he is sick. He will stay and do his work faithfully as long as he can, and we won't ask for him back a minute sooner than he can be spared. Now come and hear the letter."

They all drew to the fire, Mother in the big chair, with Beth at her feet, Meg and Amy perched on either arm of the chair, and Jo leaning on the back, where no one would see any sign of emotion if the letter should happen to be very touching. Very few letters were written in those hard times that were not touching, especially those which fathers sent home. In this one, little was said of the hardships that were endured, the dangers faced, or the homesickness conquered. It was a cheerful, hopeful letter, full of lively descriptions of camp life, marches, and military news, and only at the end did the writer's heart overflow with fatherly love and longing for the little girls at home.

Give them all my dear love and a kiss. Tell them I think of them by day, pray for them by night, and find my best comfort in their affection at all times. A year seems very long to wait before I see them, but remind them that while we wait we may all work, so that these days need not be wasted. I know they will remember all I said to them, that they will be loving children to you, will do their duty, fight their enemies bravely, and conquer themselves so beautifully that when I come back to them I may be fonder and prouder than ever of my little women.

"What in the world are you going to do now, Jo?" asked Meg one snowy afternoon, as her sister came tramping through the hall in rubber boots, old coat, and hood, with a broom in one hand and a shovel in the other.

"Going out for exercise," answered Jo with a mischievous twinkle in her eyes.

"I should think two long walks this morning would have been enough! It's cold and dull out. I advise you to stay warm and dry by the fire, as I do," said Meg with a shiver.

"Never take advice! Can't keep still all day and, not being a cat, I don't like to doze by the fire. I like adventures, and I'm going out to find some."

Meg went back to toast her feet and read, and Jo began to dig paths with great energy. The snow was light, and with her broom she soon swept a path all round the garden.

The garden separated the Marches' house from that of Mr. Laurence. A low hedge parted the two estates. On one side was an old brown house, looking rather bare and shabby. On the other side was a stately stone mansion with every sort of comfort and luxury, from the big coach house and well-kept grounds to the glimpses of lovely things one caught between the rich curtains. Yet it seemed a lonely, lifeless sort of house, for no children frolicked on the lawn, no motherly face ever smiled at the windows, and few people went in and out, except the old gentleman and his grandson.

To Jo's lively fancy, this fine house seemed a kind of enchanted palace, full of splendors and delights, which no one enjoyed. She had long wanted to behold these hidden glories and to know the "Laurence boy," who looked as if he would like to be known, if he only knew how to begin. She had met him briefly at a party, and had planned many ways of making friends with him. But he had not been seen lately, and Jo began to think he had gone away, when she one day spied a brown face at the upper window, looking wistfully down into their garden where Beth and Amy were snowballing one another.

"That boy is suffering for society and fun," she said to herself. "His grandpa does not know what's good for him and keeps him shut up all alone. He needs a party of jolly boys to play with, or somebody young and lively. I've a great mind to go over and tell the gentleman so!"

The idea amused Jo, who liked to do daring things. The plan of "going over" was not forgotten, and when the snowy afternoon came, Jo resolved to see what could be done. She saw Mr. Laurence drive off, and then sallied out. All quiet—curtains down at the lower windows; servants out of sight and nothing human visible but a curly black head leaning on a thin hand at the upper window.

"There he is," thought Jo, "poor boy! All alone and sick this dismal day. It's a shame! I'll toss up a snowball and make him look out, and then say a kind word to him."

Up went a handful of soft snow, and the head turned at once, showing a face which lost its listless look in a minute, as the big eyes and mouth began to smile. Jo nodded and laughed and called out, "How do you do? Are you sick?"

Laurie opened the window and croaked out as hoarsely as a raven, "Better, thank you. I've had a bad cold and been shut up a week."

"I'm sorry. What do you amuse yourself with?"

"Nothing. It's as dull as tombs up here."

"Don't you read?"

"Not much. They won't let me."

"Can't somebody read to you?"

"Grandpa does, sometimes; but my books don't interest him, and I hate to ask Brooke, my tutor, all the time."

"Have someone come and see you, then."

"There isn't anyone I'd like to see. Boys make such a row, and my head is weak."

"Isn't there some nice girl who'd read and amuse you? Girls are quiet, and like to play nurse."

"Don't know any."

"You know us," began Jo, then laughed and stopped.

"So I do! Will you come up, please?" cried Laurie.

"I'm not quiet and nice, but I'll come, if Mother will let me. I'll go ask her. Shut the window, like a good boy, and wait till I come."

Laurie was in a flutter of excitement at the idea of having company and flew about to get ready, trying to tidy up the room, which, in spite of half a dozen servants, was anything but neat. Presently there came a loud ring, then a decided voice asking for "Mr. Laurie," and a surprised-looking servant came running up to announce a young lady.

"All right, show her up. It's Miss Jo," said Laurie, going to the door to meet Jo, who appeared, looking rosy and kind and quite at ease, with a covered dish in one hand and Beth's three kittens in the other.

"Here I am, bag and baggage," she said briskly. "Mother sent her love, and was glad if I could do anything for you. Meg wanted me to bring some of her special dessert, and Beth thought her cats would be comforting. I knew you'd laugh at them, but I couldn't refuse, she was so anxious to do something."

It so happened that Beth's funny loan was just the thing, for in laughing over the kittens, Laurie forgot his bashfulness and grew sociable at once.

"That looks too good to eat," he said, smiling with pleasure, as Jo uncovered the dish and showed the dessert, surrounded by a garland of green leaves.

"It isn't anything, only they all felt kindly. Put it away for your tea: it's so simple, you can eat it; and, being soft, it will slip down without hurting your sore throat. What a cozy room this is!"

"It might be if it was kept nice."

"I'll right it up in two minutes; for it only needs to have the hearth brushed, so—and the things made straight on the mantelpiece, so—and the books put here, and the bottles there, and your sofa turned from the light, and the pillows plumped up a bit. Now then, you're fixed."

And so he was, for, as she laughed and talked, Jo had whisked things into place and given quite a different air to the room. Laurie watched her in respectful silence and when she beckoned him to his sofa, he sat down with a sigh of satisfaction, saying gratefully, "How kind you are! Yes, that's what it wanted. Now please take the big chair and let me do something to amuse my company."

"No. I came to amuse you. Shall I read aloud?" and Jo looked affectionately toward some inviting books near by.

"Thank you. I've read all those and, if you don't mind, I'd rather talk," answered Laurie.

"Not a bit. I'll talk all day if you'll only get me going. Beth says I never know when to stop."

"Is Beth the rosy one, who stays at home a good deal, and sometimes goes out with a little basket?" asked Laurie, with interest.

"Yes, that's Beth."

"The pretty one is Meg, and the curly-haired one is Amy, I believe?"

"How did you find out?"

Laurie colored, but answered frankly, "Why, you see, I often hear you calling to one another, and when I'm alone up here I can't help looking over at your house—you always seem to be having such good times. I beg your pardon for being so rude, but sometimes you forget to put down the curtain at the window where the flowers are. And when the lamps are lighted, it's like looking at a picture to see the fire, and you all around the table with your mother. Her face looks so sweet behind the flowers I can't help watching it. I haven't got any mother, you know." And Laurie poked the fire to hide a twitching of the lips that he could not control.

The solitary, hungry look in his eyes went straight to Jo's warm heart. Laurie was sick and lonely, and feeling how rich she was in home and happiness, she gladly tried to share it with him. Her face was very friendly and her sharp voice unusually gentle as she said, "We'll never draw that curtain any more, and I give you leave to look as much as you like. I just wish, though, instead of peeping, you'd come over and see us. Mother is so splendid, she'd do you heaps of good, and Beth would sing to you if I begged her to, and Amy would dance. Meg and I would make you laugh over the funny plays we put on, and we'd have jolly times. Wouldn't your grandpa let you?"

"I think he would, if your mother asked him. He's very kind, though he does not look so, and he lets me do what I like, pretty much, only he's afraid I might be a bother to strangers," began Laurie, brightening more and more.

"We are not strangers, we are neighbors, and you needn't think you'd be a bother. We want to know you, and I've been trying to for ever so long. We haven't been here a great while, you know, but we have got acquainted with all our neighbors but you."

"You see, Grandpa lives among his books, and doesn't mind much what happens outside. Mr. Brooke, my tutor, doesn't stay here, you know, and I have no one to go about with me, so I just stay at home and get on as I can."

"That's bad. You ought to make an effort and go visiting everywhere you are asked, then you'll have plenty of friends, and pleasant places to go to. Never mind being bashful. It won't last long if you keep going."

Laurie turned red again, but wasn't offended at being accused of bashfulness, for there was so much good will in Jo it was impossible not to take her blunt speeches as kindly as they were meant.

"Do you like your school?" asked the boy, changing the subject, after a little pause.

"Don't go to school. I'm a businessman—girl, I mean. I go to wait on my great-aunt, and a dear, cross old soul she is, too," answered Jo.

Laurie opened his mouth to ask another question, but remembering just in time that it wasn't polite to make too many inquiries into people's affairs, he shut it again, and looked uncomfortable. Jo didn't mind having a laugh at Aunt March, so she gave him a lively description of the fidgety old lady, her fat poodle, the parrot that talked Spanish, and her library. Laurie enjoyed that immensely, and when she told about the prim old gentleman who came once to woo Aunt March, and in the middle of a fine speech, how Poll had tweaked his wig off to his great dismay, the boy lay back and laughed till the tears ran down his cheeks, and a maid popped her head in to see what was the matter.

"Oh! That does me no end of good. Tell on, please," he said, taking his face out of the sofa cushion, red and shining with merriment.

Much elated with her success, Jo did "tell on," all about their plays and plans, their hopes and fears for Father, and the most interesting events of the little world in which the sisters lived. Then they got to talking about books, and to Jo's delight, she found that Laurie loved them as well as she did, and had read even more than herself.

"If you like them so much, come down and see ours. Grandfather is out, so you needn't be afraid," said Laurie, getting up.

"I'm not afraid of anything," returned Jo, with a toss of the head.

"I don't believe you are!" exclaimed the boy, looking at her with much admiration, though he privately thought she would have good reason to be a trifle afraid of the old gentleman if she met him in some of his moods.

Laurie led the way from room to room, letting Jo stop to examine whatever struck her fancy. And so at last they came to the library, where she clapped her hands and pranced, as she always did when especially delighted. It was lined with books, and there were pictures and statues, and little cabinets full of coins and curiosities.

"What richness!" sighed Jo, sinking into the depth of a velvet chair and gazing about her with an air of intense satisfaction. "Theodore Laurence, you ought to be the happiest boy in the world," she added.

"A fellow can't live on books," said Laurie, shaking his head as he perched on a table opposite.

Before he could say more, a bell rang, and Jo flew up, exclaiming with alarm, "Mercy me! It's your grandpa!"

"Well, what if it is? You are not afraid of anything, you know," returned the boy, looking wicked.

"I think I am a little bit afraid of him, but I don't know why I should be. Marmee said I might come, and I don't think you're any the worse for it," said Jo, composing herself, though she kept her eyes on the door.

"I'm a great deal better for it, and ever so much obliged. I'm only afraid you are very tired of talking to me. It was so pleasant, I couldn't bear to stop," said Laurie gratefully.

"The doctor to see you, sir," and the maid beckoned as she spoke.

"Would you mind if I left you for a minute? I suppose I must see him," said Laurie.

"Don't mind me. I'm happy as a cricket here," answered Jo.

Laurie went away, and his guest amused herself in her own way. She was standing before a fine portrait of the old gentleman, and she said decidedly, "I'm sure now that I shouldn't be afraid of him, for he's got kind eyes, though his mouth is grim, and he looks as if he had a tremendous will of his own. He isn't as handsome as my grandfather, but I like him."

"Thank you, ma'am," said a gruff voice behind her, and there, to her great dismay, stood old Mr. Laurence.

Poor Jo blushed till she couldn't blush any redder, and her heart began to beat uncomfortably fast as she thought what she had said. For a minute a wild desire to run away possessed her, but that was cowardly, so she resolved to stay and get out of the scrape as she could. A second look showed her that the living eyes, under the bushy eyebrows, were kinder even than the painted ones, and there was a sly twinkle in them, which lessened her fear a good deal. The gruff voice was gruffer than ever as the old gentleman said abruptly, "So you're not afraid of me, hey?"

"Not much, sir."

"And you don't think me as handsome as your grandfather?"

"Not quite, sir."

"And I've got a tremendous will, have I?"

"I only said I thought so."

"But you like me in spite of it?"

"Yes, I do, sir."

That answer pleased the old gentleman. He gave a short laugh, shook hands with her, and, putting his finger under her chin, turned up her face, examined it gravely, and let it go, saying with a nod, "You've got your grandfather's spirit, if you haven't his face. He was a fine man, my dear, but what is better, he was a brave and an honest one, and I was proud to be his friend."

"Thank you, sir." And Jo was quite comfortable after that, for it suited her exactly.

"What have you been doing to this boy of mine, hey?" was the next question, sharply put.

"Only trying to be neighborly, sir." And Jo told how her visit came about.

"You think he needs cheering up a bit, do you?"

"Yes, sir, he seems a little lonely, and young folks would do him good perhaps. We are only girls, but we should be glad to help if we could," said Jo eagerly.

"There's the tea bell. We have it early on the boy's account. Come down and go on being neighborly."

"If you'd like to have me, sir."

"Shouldn't ask you if I didn't." And Mr. Laurence offered her his arm with old-fashioned courtesy.

"What would Meg say to this?" thought Jo, as she was marched away, while her eyes danced with fun as she imagined herself telling the story at home.

Laurie came running downstairs and pulled up with a start of surprise at the astounding sight of Jo arm in arm with his grandfather.

"I didn't know you'd come, sir," he began, as Jo gave him a triumphant little glance.

"That's evident, by the way you racket downstairs. Come to your tea, sir, and behave like a gentleman." And having pulled the boy's hair by way of a caress, Mr. Laurence walked on, while Laurie went through a series of comic gestures behind their backs, which nearly produced an explosion of laughter from Jo.

The old gentleman did not say much as he drank his tea, but he watched the young people, who soon chatted away like old friends, and the change in his grandson did not escape him. There was color, light, and life in the boy's face now, vivacity in his manner, and genuine merriment in his laugh.

"She's right, the lad is lonely. I'll see what these little girls can do for him," thought Mr. Laurence, as he looked and listened. He liked Jo, for her odd, blunt ways suited him, and she seemed to understand the boy almost as well as if she had been one herself.

If the Laurences had been what Jo called "prim and poky," she would not have got on at all, for such people always made her shy and awkward. But finding them free and easy, she was so herself, and made a good impression. When they rose she proposed to go, but Laurie said he had something more to show her, and took her away to the conservatory, which had been lighted for her benefit.

It seemed quite fairylike to Jo, as she went up and down the walks, enjoying the blooming walls on either side, the soft light, the damp sweet air, and the wonderful vines and trees that hung about her, while her new friend cut the finest flowers till his hands were full. Then he tied them up, saying, with the happy look Jo liked to see, "Please give these to your mother, and tell her I like the medicine she sent me very much."

They found Mr. Laurence standing before the fire in the great drawing room, but Jo's attention was entirely absorbed by a grand piano, which stood open.

"Do you play?" she asked, turning to Laurie with a respectful expression.

"Sometimes," he answered modestly.

"Please do now. I want to hear it, so I can tell Beth."

"Won't you first?"

"Don't know how. Too stupid to learn, but I love music dearly."

So Laurie played and Jo listened, with her nose buried in heliotrope and tea roses. Her respect and regard for the "Laurence boy" increased very much, for he played remarkably well and didn't put on any airs. She praised him till he was quite abashed, and his grandfather came to his rescue.

"That will do, that will do, young lady. Too many sugarplums are not good for him. His music isn't bad, but I hope he will do as well in more important things. Going? Well, I'm much obliged to you, and I hope you'll come again. My respects to your mother. Good night, Doctor Jo."

He shook hands kindly, but looked as if something did not please him. When they got into the hall, Jo asked Laurie if she had said something amiss. He shook his head.

"No, it was me. He doesn't like to hear me play."

"Why not?"

"I'll tell you some day."

"Take care of yourself, won't you?"

"Yes, but you will come again, I hope?"

"If you promise to come and see us after you are well."

"I will."

"Good night, Laurie!"

"Good night, Jo, good night!"

When Jo returned home and told all the afternoon's adventures, the family all wished to visit, for each found something very attractive in the big house on the other side of the hedge. Mrs. March wanted to talk of her father with the old man who had not forgotten him. Meg longed to walk in the conservatory. Beth sighed for the grand piano. And Amy was eager to see the fine pictures and statues.

"Mother, why didn't Mr. Laurence like to have Laurie play?" asked Jo.

"I am not sure, but I think it was because his son, Laurie's father, married an Italian lady, a musician, which displeased the old man, who is very proud. The lady was good and lovely and accomplished, but he did not like her, and never saw his son after he married. They both died when Laurie was a little child, and then his grandfather took him home.

Laurie comes naturally by his love of music, for he is like his mother, and I dare say his skill reminds him of the woman he did not like."

"Dear me, how romantic!" exclaimed Meg.

"How silly!" said Jo. "Let him be a musician if he wants to, and not plague his life out sending him to college, if he hates to go."

"That's why he has such handsome black eyes and pretty manners, I suppose. Italians are always nice," said Meg, who was a little sentimental.

"What do you know about his eyes and his manners? You never spoke to him, hardly," cried Jo, who was not sentimental.

"I saw him at the party, and what you tell shows that he knows how to behave. That was a nice little speech about the medicine Mother sent him."

"He meant the dessert, I suppose."

"How stupid you are! He meant you, of course."

"Did he?" And Jo opened her eyes as if it had never occurred to her before.

"I never saw such a girl! You don't know a compliment when you get it," said Meg, with the air of a young lady who knew all about the matter.

"I think they are great nonsense, and I'll thank you not to be silly and spoil my fun. Laurie's a nice boy and I like him, and I won't have any sentimental stuff about compliments and such rubbish. We'll all be good to him because he hasn't got any mother, and he may come over and see us, mayn't he, Marmee?"

"Yes, Jo, your little friend is very welcome, and I hope Meg will remember that children should be children as long as they can."

Meg stood at the window one dull afternoon, looking out at the frostbitten garden, and feeling out of sorts. "Nothing pleasant ever happens in this family," she said. "We go grubbing along day after day, without a bit of change, and very little fun. We might as well be in a treadmill."

Beth, who sat at the other window, said, smiling, "Two pleasant things are going to happen right away. Marmee is coming down the street, and Laurie is tramping through the garden as if he had something nice to tell."

In they both came. Mrs. March asked her usual question: "Any letter from Father, girls?"

Laurie asked in his persuasive way, "Won't some of you come for a drive? I've been working away at mathematics till my head is in a muddle. Come, Jo, you and Beth will go, won't you?"

"We three will be ready in a minute!" cried Amy.

"Can I do anything for you?" asked Laurie, leaning over Mrs. March's chair with the affectionate look and tone he always gave her.

"No, thank you, except call at the office, if you'll be so kind, dear. It's our day for a letter, and the postman has brought nothing. Father is as regular as the sun, but perhaps there's some delay."

A sharp ring interrupted Mrs. March, and a minute after, Hannah, who was considered by the family more as a friend than a servant, came in with a letter.

"It's one of those horrid telegraph things, mum," she said, handing it as if she was afraid it would explode and do some damage.

At the word "telegraph," Mrs. March snatched it, read the two lines it contained, and dropped back into her chair as white as if the little paper had sent a bullet to her heart. Laurie dashed downstairs for water, while Meg and Hannah supported her, and Jo read aloud in a frightened voice:

MRS. MARCH:
Your husband is very ill. Come at once.
S. HALE, Blank Hospital, Washington

How still the room was as they listened breathlessly. How strangely the day darkened outside. How suddenly the whole world seemed to change as the girls gathered about their mother, feeling as if all the happiness and support of their lives was about to be taken from them.

Mrs. March was herself again directly. She read the message over, and stretched out her arms to her daughters, saying, in a tone they never forgot, "I shall go at once, but it may be too late. Oh children, children, help me to bear it!"

For several minutes there was nothing but the sound of sobbing in the room, mingled with broken words of comfort, tender assurances of help, and hopeful whispers that died away in tears. Poor Hannah was the first to recover.

"The Lord keep the dear man! I won't waste no time cryin', but git your things ready right away, mum," she said heartily, as she wiped her face on her apron and went away to work like three women in one.

"She's right; there's no time for tears now. Be calm, girls, and let me think."

They tried to be calm, poor things, as their mother sat up, looking pale but steady, and put away her grief to think and plan for them.

"Where's Laurie?" she asked when she had collected her thoughts.

"Here, ma'am. Oh, let me do something!" cried the boy, hurrying from the next room, where he had withdrawn, feeling that their first sorrow was too sacred for even his friendly eyes to see.

"Send a telegram saying I will come at once. The next train goes early in the morning. I'll take that."

"What else? The horses are ready. I can go anywhere, do anything," he said, looking ready to fly to the ends of the earth.

"Leave a note at Aunt March's. Jo, give me that pen and paper."

Jo drew the table before her mother, well knowing that money for the long sad journey must be borrowed from Aunt March, and feeling as if she would do anything to add a little sum for her father.

"Now go, dear. But don't kill yourself driving at a desperate pace; there is no need of that."

Mrs. March's warning was evidently thrown away, for five minutes later Laurie tore by the window on his own fleet horse, riding as if for his life.

"Jo, run to tell Mrs. King that I can't come. On the way, get these things. I'll write them down; they'll be needed, and I must go prepared for nursing. Beth, go and ask Mr. Laurence for a couple of bottles of old wine—I'm not too proud to beg for Father. Amy, tell Hannah to get down the black trunk. And, Meg, come and help me find my things, for I'm half bewildered."

Meg begged her to sit quietly in her room for a little while and let them work. Everyone scattered like leaves before a gust of wind, and the quiet, happy household was broken up suddenly as if the paper had been an evil spell.

Mr. Laurence came hurrying back with Beth, bringing every comfort the kind old gentleman could think of for the invalid, and friendly promises of protection for the girls during their mother's absence.

As Meg ran through the entry with a cup of tea, she came suddenly upon Laurie's tutor, Mr. Brooke, whom she had met on other occasions.

"I'm very sorry to hear of this, Miss March," he said in a kind, quiet tone that soothed her perturbed spirit. "I came to offer myself as escort to your mother. It will give me real satisfaction to be of service to her."

Meg put out her hand with a face so full of gratitude that Mr. Brooke would have felt repaid for a much greater sacrifice than the trifling one of time and comfort which he was about to make.

"How kind you all are! Mother will accept, I'm sure, and it will be such a relief to know that she has someone to take care of her. Thank you very, very much!"

Meg spoke earnestly, and forgot herself entirely till something in the brown eyes looking down at her made her remember the cooling tea and lead the way into the parlor.

Everything was arranged by the time Laurie returned with a note from Aunt March, enclosing the desired sum, and a few lines repeating what she had often said before—that she had always told them it was absurd for March to go into the army, always predicted that no good would come of it, and she hoped they would take her advice next time. Mrs. March put the note in the fire and the money in her pocket, with her lips folded tightly in a way that Jo would have understood if she had been there.

The short afternoon wore away. Meg and her mother were busy at some necessary needlework, while Beth and Amy got tea, and Hannah finished her ironing. But still Jo did not come.

They began to get anxious, and Laurie went off to find her, for no one ever knew what strange idea Jo might take into her head.

He missed her, however, and she came walking in with a very strange expression, for there was a mixture of fun and fear, satisfaction and regret in it, which puzzled the family as much as did the roll of bills she laid before her mother, saying, with a little choke in her voice, "That's my contribution towards making Father comfortable and bringing him home!"

"My dear, where did you get it? Twenty-five dollars! Jo, I hope you haven't done anything rash?"

"No, it's mine honestly. I didn't beg, borrow, or steal it. I earned it. And I don't think you'll blame me, for I only sold what was my own."

As she spoke, Jo took off her bonnet, and a general outcry arose, for all her abundant hair was cut short.

"Your hair! Your beautiful hair!"

"Oh Jo, how could you? Your one beauty!"

"My dear girl, there was no need for this."

"She doesn't look like my Jo anymore, but I love her dearly for it!"

As everyone exclaimed, and Beth hugged the cropped head tenderly, Jo assumed an indifferent air, which did not deceive anyone a particle, and said, trying to look as if she liked it, "It doesn't affect the fate of the nation, so don't wail, Beth. It will be good for my vanity. I was getting too proud of my long hair. It will do my brains good to have that mop taken off. My head feels deliciously light and cool, and the barber said I could soon have a curly crop, which will be boyish, becoming, and easy to keep in order. I'm satisfied. So please take the money, and let's have supper."

"Tell me all about it, Jo. I am not quite satisfied, but I can't blame you, for I know how willingly you sacrificed your vanity, as you call it, to your love. But, my dear, it was not necessary, and I'm afraid you will regret it one of these days," said Mrs. March.

"No, I won't!" returned Jo stoutly.

"What made you do it?" asked Amy, who would as soon have thought of cutting off her head as her pretty hair.

"Well, I was wild to do something for Father," replied Jo, as they gathered about the table. "I hate to borrow as much as Mother does, and I knew Aunt March would croak—she always does, if you ask for a ninepence. I hadn't the least idea of selling my hair at first, but as I went along I kept thinking what I could do and feeling as if I'd like to dive into some of the rich stores and help myself. In a barber's window I saw tails of hair with the prices marked. And one black tail, not so thick as mine, was forty dollars. It came over me all of a sudden that I had one thing to make money out of, and without stopping to think, I walked in, asked if they bought hair, and what they would give for mine."

"I don't see how you dared to do it," said Beth in a tone of awe.

"Oh, he was a little man who looked as if he merely lived to oil his hair. He rather stared, at first, as if he wasn't used to having girls bounce into his shop and ask him to buy their hair. He said he didn't care about mine, it wasn't the fashionable color, and he'd never pay much for it in the first place. It was getting late, and I was afraid, if it wasn't done right away, that I shouldn't have done it at all, and you know when I start to do a thing I hate to give it up. So I begged him to take it, and told him why I was in such a hurry. It was silly, I dare say, but it changed his mind, for I got rather excited, and told the story in my topsy-turvy way, and his wife heard and said so kindly, 'Take it, Thomas, and oblige the young lady; I'd do as much for our Jimmy any day if I had hair worth selling.'"

"Who was Jimmy?" asked Amy, who liked to have things explained as they went along.

"Her son, she said, who was in the army. How friendly such things make strangers feel, don't they? She talked away all the time the man clipped, and diverted my mind nicely."

"Didn't you feel dreadful when the first cut came?" asked Meg with a shiver.

"I took a last, long look at my hair while the man got his things, and that was the end of it. I never snivel over trifles like that. I will confess, though, I felt odd when I saw the dear old hair laid out on the table, and felt only the short, rough ends on my head. It almost seemed as if I'd had an arm or leg cut off. The woman saw me look at it, and picked out a long lock for me to keep. I'll give it to you, Marmee, just to remember past glories by."

Mrs. March folded the wavy chestnut lock, and laid it away with a short gray one on her desk. She only said, "Thank you, deary," but something in her face made the girls change the subject, and talk as cheerfully as they could about the prospect of a fine day tomorrow, and the happy times they would have when Father came home to be nursed.

No one wanted to go to bed when, at ten o'clock, Mrs. March put by the last finished job and said, "Come, girls." Beth went to the piano and played Father's favorite hymn. All began bravely, but broke down one by one, till Beth was left alone, singing with all her heart, for to her music was always a sweet consoler.

"Go to bed, and don't talk, for we must be up early, and shall need all the sleep we can get. Goodnight, my darlings," said Mrs. March, as the hymn ended.

They kissed her quietly, and went to bed as silently as if the dear invalid lay in the next room. Beth and Amy soon fell asleep in spite of the great trouble, but Meg lay awake, thinking the most serious thoughts she had ever known in her short life. Jo lay motionless, and her sister fancied that she was asleep, till a stifled sob made her exclaim, "Jo, dear, what is it? Are you crying about Father?"

"No, not now."

"What then?"

"My—my hair!" burst out poor Jo, with a choke. "I'd do it again tomorrow, if I could. It's only the vain, selfish part of me that goes and cries in this silly way. Don't tell anyone, it's all over now. I thought you were asleep, so I just made a little private moan for my one beauty. Why are you awake?"

"I can't sleep, I'm so anxious," said Meg.

"Think about something pleasant, and soon you'll drop off."

"I tried it, but felt wider awake than ever."

"What did you think of?"

"Handsome faces—eyes particularly," answered Meg, smiling to herself, in the dark.

"What color do you like best?"

"Brown—that is, sometimes; blue are lovely."

Jo laughed, and Meg sharply ordered her not to talk, then amiably promised to make her hair curl, and fell asleep to dream of living in her castle in the air.

The clocks were striking midnight and the rooms were very still as a figure glided quietly from bed to bed, smoothing a cover here, settling a pillow there, and pausing to look long and tenderly at each unconscious face, to kiss each with lips that mutely blessed, and to pray the fervent prayers which only mothers utter.

LIFE STORIES: YOUNG AND BRAVE

A Ride in the Night

from Will Clark, Boy Adventurer
by Katharine E. Wilkie

*In 1803, the third president of the United States, Thomas
Jefferson, made a deal called the Louisiana Purchase, in which he
bought the North American lands claimed by France. This
single purchase almost doubled the size of our country. The land
stretched from the Mississippi River west to the Rocky Mountains.
When Thomas Jefferson wanted to know more about this land,
he sent a group of men to explore it, led by Meriwether Lewis and
William Clark.*

*William Clark was born in Virginia in 1770. He was the sixth
son in the family. All his older brothers fought in the American
Revolution. One of his brothers, George Rogers Clark, led a group
of soldiers fighting the British in Kentucky.*

*Here is a story about an adventure that young Will Clark had
during the Revolutionary War. In this story, you'll also meet York,
a slave owned by the Clark family, who was about the same age as
Will. When York grew up, he went with Captain William Clark as
an important member of the team that explored the American West.*

1

It was 1779. Will Clark had grown into a tall boy of nine.
Today he stood facing his father in the dining room of their
Virginia home.

"He's too young," Ann Clark said quickly to her husband.

John Clark frowned. He was sitting in a big armchair with
one foot on a stool in front of him. He looked hard at Will.
"Yes, he's too young," John Clark agreed.

"But I can do it, Father," Will Clark said.

"Those horses must be delivered," Mr. Clark said slowly.

"But he's only a boy, John," his wife insisted.

Mr. Clark looked at Will. Few boys of his age were as tall and as broad-shouldered as this red-haired, blue-eyed lad. He could easily have been mistaken for eleven.

"This boy can do it," John Clark answered at last. "I know he can."

Will could hardly keep back a shout. He was really going to be trusted with this job.

"Listen carefully to me," said John Clark. "You must carry out my directions to the letter. Oh, if only I had not dropped that stone on my foot last week!"

"Don't worry, Father," said Will. "I'll do exactly as you say."

John Clark's voice dropped almost to a whisper. "You'll take the string of six horses to the ford at Plover's Creek. There you'll cross and follow the trail to Sugar Maple Hill. On the far side of the hill is a small tavern run by a man named Coleman. I've never seen him, so I can't describe him to you. But the password is 'Kentucky,' so don't give the horses to anyone who doesn't give it to you."

"Kentucky!"

"Hush!" commanded John Clark. "What better password is there for a man with a son on the Kentucky frontier?"

"And we'll go there someday," Will reminded him. "You promised, and so did George."

His father nodded. "Meanwhile, you must get those horses delivered. They'll be used in the Continental Army. General

Washington needs them. He needs all the help every patriot can give. Take York with you. Sometimes two heads are better than one."

Will started out of the room on a run. His mother called him back. She looked at her youngest son for a long time. "Now I have six sons serving their country," she said softly.

Fifteen minutes later Will and York were riding away from home in the moonlight. Besides their own mounts, they had six horses to be delivered to Coleman's Inn.

Neither boy knew too well the part of the country to which he was going. But Will was certain he could find the place.

"You must be part bloodhound." York chuckled. "I'll bet you could find your way to Kentucky all by yourself."

"I'd like to try," Will answered. "But by the time I go, the route will be well marked."

"I won't mind if it is," said York. "You'll take me with you, won't you?"

"Of course. When the war is over, all of us are going. All my family and all yours. We'll make quite a procession, won't we? By that time my five brothers will be home from the army. I suppose they'll go, too. And of course there are Elizabeth, Lucy, Fanny, and Ann."

"I wish we were there now in a nice, warm house. It's cold out here tonight," said York with a shiver. His teeth chattered as he spoke. Somewhere in the distance a hoot owl gave a mournful sound. "Listen!"

"At least you know that's not an Indian on the warpath. All the Indians in Virginia are friendly ones," said Will. "Do you remember how the other boys and I used to imitate Indian calls and follow every traveler who came through the woods near home?"

"Yes, I do," York answered. "Look. Yonder is the ford."

In the distance Plover's Creek flowed peacefully in the moonlight. The boys had been riding for several hours. They were glad to come to this stage in their journey. The path to the ford lay clear and shining before them.

"Come on!" called Will. He kicked his horse's side slightly. "You follow behind, York, just to be certain everything is all right."

In a few minutes the boys rode up out of the water. The wet coats of the horses shone in the moonlight. The trail toward Sugar Maple Hill was clearly to be seen.

Will shivered slightly. "That water was chilly. I'll be glad to deliver these horses and warm myself before a good fire."

York sighed. "It seems as if I can taste Mama's bacon and hominy grits right now. I'm hungry."

"So am I," agreed his companion. "It can't be much longer now, York."

2

Nearly an hour later the boys looked down from a little rise into the valley below. They saw a large tavern. Smoke was curling from the chimney, even though the hour was early.

"There's our breakfast," York said hungrily. "What are we waiting for?"

"I don't know," Will said slowly. "There's something I don't like. I'm not certain what it is. Look, York." He pointed to a half dozen horses tied outside the tavern. "Father said I should see a man. There's more than one man in the tavern."

"Well, after all, people do spend the night at taverns," York reminded him.

Will frowned. "Maybe I'm being extra careful, but I'm not going to take these horses down there yet. You lead them back into the woods and wait for me."

"All right," York grumbled. "But don't forget my stomach has just about grown to my backbone. I'm hungry!"

York turned with all the horses and led them into the surrounding woods. Will rode alone down to the tavern.

He dismounted outside the door. Then he tied his mare to the hitching rack with all the other horses. His heart was beating fast as he entered the building.

Once inside the main room he looked quickly about him. What he feared was true: a group of red-coated soldiers were sitting around a large pine table.

"Here's a new man for King George!" one of them called loudly.

Will swallowed hard as they turned to look at him. The British soldiers with their mugs and platters looked as big as giants. The landlord leaned over the counter. He had a long, sharp carving knife in his hand.

The boy tried to speak. For a moment his voice would not come. "I d-don't think the King could use me yet," he stammered.

Most of the men roared with laughter. They seemed to think the idea of Will being a soldier was very funny.

"He doesn't think the King could use him yet!" repeated one of the men. "He's right. King George doesn't want fighters as young as he is. Ha! Ha! Ha!"

Another soldier was watching Will closely. This man had not laughed so much as his companions. "What are you doing out so early, boy?" he demanded.

Will gave a start. He hoped the man did not notice it. He did some fast thinking. "I'm on the way to my aunt's house, sir."

"Where does she live?" asked the soldier. He kept his eyes fixed on Will.

"At Williamsburg."

"And you're going there alone?"

"There's no one to go with me. I'm an orphan. I spend half the time with my aunt, half the time with my grandmother down in the country," Will added.

He stole a glance at the other men. They were paying little attention to him. They were too busy talking and laughing and eating. Then the questioning soldier turned to them. "This boy may know something about the horses."

Will's heart was in his mouth. He had been right after all: there was something wrong here somewhere.

The man was still talking. "He may even have brought them with him."

"Nonsense, Brown!" insisted another man. "He's only a boy. No one would trust valuable horses to a boy!"

The soldier called Brown turned toward Will. His eyes were cold and dangerous. He twisted Will's shoulder crudely. "We're on the lookout for horses intended for the Continental Army. Do you know anything about them?"

"Ouch! You're hurting me!"

The man's roughness had brought real tears to Will's eyes. The boy was glad of it. The pain would excuse the look of fear on his face. But his great fear was for York, hidden back in the woods with the horses.

"Stop it, Brown," one of the men ordered. "I have a son at home about his age. You shan't mistreat this boy."

Brown scowled. "Even boys can be traitors. How do I know he isn't a lying little rebel?"

"Shut up, I tell you!" said the other soldier. "This lad knows nothing about any horses. Eat your breakfast, boy, and be on your way."

Will could hardly swallow the plate of ham and eggs that the innkeeper brought him. This man, too, gave him a keen look that did nothing to relieve his uneasiness. Could he be the Mr. Coleman of whom his father had spoken? It didn't seem so from the way he scowled. He didn't look friendly at all.

As soon as Will had finished, he laid a coin on the table and stole out the door. Once astride his mare, he turned her head toward the woods.

"That's not the road to Williamsburg," a voice growled from the doorway.

The boy looked down to meet the scowling eyes of his enemy. "I was only getting my bearings. I know the road to Williamsburg."

He galloped off in the opposite direction of the one he wanted to take. York must wait with the horses. Will hoped with all his heart that the boy would remain hidden in the woods.

Once out of site of the tavern, Will slid out of the saddle. He patted the mare's muzzle and led her off the road into the underbrush. "We won't have a trail to follow this time, girl," he told her. "But somehow we must get back to York and those horses."

The distance back was short, but the going was rough. The way was tangled with sharp briars and thick undergrowth. Several times Will became a little confused.

Finally, however, he came to the spot where York sat in a little clearing. Will drew a breath of relief when he saw him. The horses were standing quietly nearby.

"I thought you had deserted me," York moaned. "I thought I'd have to stay out here in these woods until I starved to death."

"That might be better than a rope around your neck," Will told him grimly. "That tavern is filled with British soldiers. I had trouble getting away from them."

York's eyes opened wide. "What shall we do now?" he asked.

"We must wait for them to leave," Will said. "We'll take turns watching. They'll have to be on their way before long."

The sun was high in the sky before the soldiers came out the tavern door. They mounted their horses and galloped away toward the north. The boys waited in the woods a while longer. At last they made their way slowly and cautiously down to the tavern.

That landlord's face lighted up with a smile as Will came in the door.

"So it's you again," he said. "You wouldn't be from Kentucky, would you?"

He said the word so loud and clearly that Will knew he had come to the end of his journey.

"No, I'm not from Kentucky," he answered. He too lingered on the word. "Neither are the horses hidden back in the woods, but maybe you'd like to have them anyway."

The landlord gave a hearty laugh. He laid a friendly hand on Will's shoulder. "That I would," he said. "I've been looking for them, and my son Edward will take them on their way tonight. My name is George Coleman."

Will gave a happy sigh. He had completed his mission successfully. He had finished the job. Now he could go home.

"I thought it was all over when you walked in on the King's men," said Mr. Coleman. "It wasn't safe for me to give you a signal of any kind. But you played your part well. You're a bright lad—a lad to help build America."

Will smiled as he and York rode away from the tavern toward home. He was proud because of Mr. Coleman's praise. But most of all he was proud because he had done something to help carry on the war.

YOUNG FREDERICK DOUGLASS: THE SLAVE WHO LEARNED TO READ

by Linda Walvoord Girard

In 1826 eight-year-old Frederick Bailey arrived in Baltimore. He had been sent from a plantation in the country to be the slave of Hugh Auld, his wife Sophia (or "Miz Sopha," as Frederick called her), and their young son Tommy.

For the first time in his life, Frederick had a straw bed and enough to eat. He wore trousers instead of a tattered, knee-length shirt, and instead of scooping his meals from a trough, he sat at a dinner table. And his mistress was very kind.

After dinner Mrs. Auld would often get her Bible and read aloud. One night, when Mr. Auld was gone, she read from the Book of Job. Suddenly, Frederick understood that the marks on a page could tell a story. He gathered his courage and asked Miz Sopha to teach him to read. Since she was getting ready to teach Tommy the ABCs anyway, Mrs. Auld agreed that Frederick could listen.

One day Mr. Auld came home while Mrs. Auld was teaching the boys. Miz Sopha bragged that Frederick was learning to read, and wasn't it amazing? Wasn't it amusing?

Mr. Auld sent Frederick out of the room. Then he began to lecture his wife. Teaching a slave was against the law, he told her. A slave who could read would be "spoiled." He would get ideas. He'd want to write as well, and if he could write, there was no telling what mischief he'd dream up. From his listening place outside the door, Frederick heard Mrs. Auld promise never to teach him again.

Now that he knew reading was forbidden, Frederick was determined to learn. If a newspaper was blowing about in the street, Frederick picked it up. If somebody left a schoolbook on the playground, it went home with him. And on errands, he studied street names and the packages and signs in stores. He spelled things out, and his reading got smoother and faster.

White schoolboys who had become his friends told him to get a book of great speeches called the *Columbian Orator*. In that book, they said, a slave debates his master and wins his freedom!

Frederick blacked boots to get the fifty cents he needed. He walked to a bookstore and bought the *Columbian Orator*. In it he discovered eloquent speeches from history, including the dialogue between master and slave. He read the speeches over and over until he understood them all. But could a slave truly win freedom by argument? he wondered. Would whites listen if a slave spoke? As his master, Mr. Auld, had feared, this slave had gotten ideas.

Frederick often played and did chores in the shipyards of Baltimore. He watched as the carpenters sawed and shaped pieces of lumber. On each piece, they wrote the initials for a part of the ship.

"What's that, Massa?" Frederick would ask.

"That's the letter *S*."

"Oh, the letter *S*. And what does that mean?"

"Means 'starboard.'"

"*S*, starboard. Yes, Massa, I'll remember that," he'd say. "And what's that, Massa?"

"The letter *L* – 'larboard.'"

"Why, I'll remember that, Massa." And so on.

When the carpenters went to eat, Frederick would copy the letters. He knew if he could learn a few letters, he could learn the rest as well.

Often, when Frederick met white boys, he would suggest a writing contest. Using chalk, he'd draw the letters he knew on the pavement or on a wall. "Beat that if you can," he'd say.

The other boys would scrawl letters he didn't know, laughing at the idea that a slave boy could win a writing contest. Frederick lost the contests. But he would copy the new letters.

In the evening, in his small room above the kitchen, Frederick struggled on. He copied the tiny letters from a hymn book and a Bible he'd found in the house. He "borrowed" Tommy's old copybooks—small booklets in which students practiced penmanship. Frederick made his own practice letters in the empty spaces under Tommy's writing. He could have been whipped for messing up Tommy's precious keepsake schoolbooks, but luckily he was not found out. He slipped the books back into their places, and no one ever noticed the extra writing. By the time he was thirteen, Frederick could read and write very well.

A year later Frederick was given to a new master—Hugh Auld's brother, Thomas, who lived in the village of St. Michael's, Maryland.

When other slaves in St. Michael's learned that Frederick could read, they asked him to teach a Sunday school. The class met secretly in a free black man's house where there were desks, spelling books, and Bibles. During the second week, Thomas Auld burst in with a white mob. The men broke up the school with clubs and warned the students never to meet again.

Thomas Auld sent Frederick to a cruel slave "breaker" named Edward Covey. Frederick worked in Covey's fields from dawn to dark. Covey often whipped him for no reason. Soon Frederick's back was covered with scars, and he nearly lost an eye from a beating.

One hot summer morning, Covey started to beat him again. Frederick fought back. "I won't let you beat me," he said over and over. Their struggle lasted two hours. To Frederick's amazement, Covey finally gave up and never tried to beat him again.

When Frederick's year with Covey came to an end, Thomas Auld hired him out to a farmer named William Freeland. Then he lent him back to his brother Hugh in Baltimore.

Starving for educated companionship, Frederick joined a club of free young black people called the East Baltimore Mental Improvement Society. Tall and poised, the handsome Frederick Bailey stood out in the group. It was here that he met a special, gentle young woman named Anna Murray.

Meanwhile, Hugh Auld decided to "rent" Frederick in the shipyards. Each Friday Frederick had to hand his master his wages—at first $6.50 a week, later $9.00. That was more than some of the white dockworkers earned, and once, jealous workers severely beat him. His life had become impossible. And as long as he was a slave, he could never marry Anna. Slaves could not sign papers or make legal ties such as marriage.

When he was twenty, Frederick decided to make a daring escape. With money Anna lent him, he would buy a ticket and go north by train.

Frederick knew that a black person traveling north would have to show papers proving he or she was free. And "free papers" were legal documents with official seals. Frederick couldn't fake these.

A good friend, a free black sailor named Benny, lent Frederick his sailor's "protection paper." This showed that Benny was registered as a seaman with an American shipping company. Across the top of this certificate, a big American eagle spread its wings. Below was a description of Benny.

It was a risky plan. If Frederick were caught, he would be sold south into harsh slavery. And Benny could go to jail.

Frederick made his run for freedom on September 3, 1838. He promised to write Anna as soon as he was safe. Because she was free, she could come north to meet him.

Frederick carefully planned every detail. He wore a sailor's red shirt, tarpaulin hat, and black neckerchief, loosely tied. He knew it could be dangerous for a black man to wait in the station with luggage, so he hired a cabdriver to race the train with his bag and toss it to him at the very last moment.

With Benny's paper, he settled into the "Negro car." His heart was pounding, but he acted calm.

The conductor came through and checked the papers of several free black passengers. "I suppose you have your free papers?" he asked Frederick.

"I never carry my free papers to sea with me," said Frederick. "I have a paper with the American eagle on it that will carry me around the world." With this he pulled out the impressive-looking sailor's protection paper. The conductor never checked to see if Frederick matched the description of the paper's owner.

Frederick's luck held, and the day after his escape, he arrived in New York City. His money was nearly gone, and he had to sleep on the docks one night. But friendly sailors warned him that the docks were patrolled for runaways, and the next night a sailor named Stewart took him to find David Ruggles, a free black abolitionist in New York.

While staying with Ruggles, Frederick wrote to Anna. She hurried north, and they were married on the 15th of September.

For safety, Frederick changed his name from Bailey to Douglass, and shortly afterward he got a job in a shipyard in New Bedford, Massachusetts. In his spare time, he began speaking about his life as a slave and the evil of a system that bought and sold human beings. He toured New England states as a speaker for the Massachusetts Anti-Slavery Society. Eloquent and passionate, Douglass held his audiences spellbound.

Because of his eloquence, many people did not believe that Douglass had ever been illiterate and a slave. To convince the doubters, in 1845 he published an autobiography, the *Narrative of the Life of Frederick Douglass.* In it he revealed his slave name and the name and location of his master. Now he was in greater danger of being seized and returned to slavery. He left for England, where he stayed for two years giving lectures for the abolitionist cause. In 1846 English friends bought his freedom from Thomas and Hugh Auld for about $700.

A year later Frederick and Anna moved to Rochester, New York, where Douglass established the *North Star,* an antislavery newspaper. Their home became a station on the Underground Railroad.

Douglass continued to work for the rights of black people. He fought for job equality and for integration in schools and churches and on trains. When traveling, he would sit in one of the railroad cars reserved for white passengers. Sometimes angry railroad workers dragged him out of his seat.

During the Civil War, he met Abraham Lincoln. "I know who you are, Mr. Douglass," the president told him. Lincoln had read the *North Star* when he was a young, unknown lawyer in Illinois. Now the president and the former slave discussed the slaves Lincoln would soon free.

Douglass went on to become Recorder of Deeds in the District of Columbia and later served as U.S. minister to Haiti. He also wrote two more autobiographies.

By the time of his death, Frederick Douglass, the slave who'd taught himself to read and write, had become the most important black leader of his time. Writer, orator, publisher, reformer, and statesman, he died in 1895 at the age of seventy-eight.

RUN, KATE SHELLEY, RUN

by Julia Pferdehirt

Kate Shelley's home stood on a hill above Honey Creek and the railroad line that led to Moingona, Iowa. All her life Kate had heard the rush of water and the whistle of trains. All her life she had watched the Chicago and Northwestern Railway cars and heard the hissing, black steam engines clack-clattering over Honey Creek Bridge.

Every train had a number and a whistle. When Kate's Pa was alive, he had taught her to recognize each train engine by the sound of its whistle. He'd been a section foreman for the Chicago and Northwestern until his death three years earlier in a railroad accident. After that, Kate and her mother fed the livestock, planted the garden, and sent the little ones off to school.

Kate was fifteen years old in July 1881, when the great storm began. It rained on Friday. By Saturday, market day, the ground was muddy, and still the rain poured down. On Sunday the roads were thick, brown sponges, sucking at boots and wagon wheels. The rain fell day and night. The following Wednesday, the sky paused to catch its breath. The day was oven-hot. Kate rushed to hang laundry to dry before the rain came again. Sure enough, by afternoon she saw more clouds, dark as midnight, rolling toward Honey Creek.

After nearly a week of rain, the creek was a wild bull, roaring and leaping, crashing against the high bluffs that caged it in on either side. Fence posts, rocks, and entire trees rolled and tumbled down the creek bed, colliding with the pilings of the bridge, causing it to creak and sway. Then the storm broke, and rain poured from the sky. The water rose.

The rising floodwaters began to seep into the barn, and Kate hurried down the hill to rescue the stock. She turned the animals out to higher ground and scrambled to save the baby pigs huddled on a haystack surrounded by water. Then Kate went up to the house and stared anxiously out the windows with her mother and nine-year-old sister, Mayme. The younger children were asleep.

It was nearly eleven o'clock when Kate heard Number 11's whistle. Long, short—long, short—screaming into the wind. The rumble of the engine grew louder as it crept along the line from Moingona to Boone, checking for washouts on the track. Suddenly Kate heard a crack like thunder, and another and another. With a sound like cannon fire, the Honey Creek trestle bridge, the engine, and four terrified crewmen crashed into the roaring water twenty feet below.

Kate pulled on her barn coat and a battered straw hat. "I'm going," she said.

Kate's mother gripped her arm. "No, Kate. You could be killed in that storm!"

Kate grabbed Pa's railroad lantern. "If Pa were out there, I'd go," she said. "I have to do it, Ma." With shaking hands, she lit the lantern and ran into the downpour and darkness to Honey Creek.

The water tossed trees and twisted metal like toys. Two men clung to branches surrounded by the wreckage; they were screaming for help. The two other crewmen had been washed away. Kate waved her lantern to say, "Hold on. Just hold on. I'll do something."

Before Kate could think of a way to help the men, a terrible thought struck her. The midnight express was scheduled to come in less than an hour. The train, its crew, and two hundred passengers were right now, right this minute, headed toward Honey Creek, not realizing that the bridge was out. It had sounded like cannon fire when Number 11 went down. It would sound like an entire war if the midnight express crashed into Honey Creek. Over two hundred people could die. She had to stop that train!

Kate gripped the lantern tighter and stumbled along the rails, following them like a road into the blackness and storm. She ran and fell, slipped and stumbled, toward the Moingona railroad station over a mile away.

Kate's chest burned. She was wet clear through and shaking with cold, but she could not stop. If it were Pa hanging on in Honey Creek or driving the midnight express, she would keep going. I must reach the station in time, she thought.

Between Honey Creek and the Moingona station, the railroad crossed the Des Moines River. The trestle bridge was high above the water and nearly seven hundred feet long. Kate dared not think of the railroad ties, a pace apart, only rain and sky between them and the river below.

The storm shook the Des Moines River bridge until it swayed and trembled. The rain fell even harder. Mud and water made the crossties slick and treacherous. How could anyone cross this bridge—caught between the wind, the rain, and the boiling, angry river?

Kate knelt down and crawled forward on her hands and knees. If it were Pa driving the midnight express toward Honey Creek, she would keep crawling. She could crawl for those two hundred people.

The wind blew her lantern out. She crept forward in the dark, feeling the railroad ties with her hands, using the cold metal rails as a guide.

Suddenly lightning flashed, and Kate saw a tree hurtling toward the bridge. Its tangled branches and massive trunk rolled and bounced in the current. It would hit the bridge! She remembered the crack of the pilings at Honey Creek and the cannon shot as the trestle collapsed. Kate clung to the crossties and prayed.

At the last second the current flipped the tree so the great trunk and its reaching limbs slipped between the pilings. Even then the branches tried to pull Kate from her perch above the river. She held on tighter and trembled.

"Only a little farther," Kate told herself when her hands finally felt mud and stones instead of empty air between the ties. She was safe across the bridge now; it was a half-mile to the station.

When she saw the station lights, Kate ran like a wild woman. Her wet skirt slapped and caught against her legs. Every breath hurt. She crashed into the station door and fell inside.

"Stop! Stop the train!" she gasped. "The engine—Honey Creek. Stop the train."

"The girl's crazy!" said one of the railroad men.

"Not on your life!" said the station agent. "That's Shelley's girl Kate."

Between gasps of air, Kate told them the Honey Creek Bridge had collapsed. "Two men are still alive," she said. "And the midnight express must be stopped."

The station agent telegraphed six miles west to Ogden to be sure the midnight express would not be allowed to continue in the storm. Then the railroad men and Kate borrowed a pusher engine and headed toward Honey Creek, blowing the whistle all the way, calling to the two stranded men to hold on a little longer.

At Honey Creek the bluffs had collapsed into the water. Kate led the rescuers to another bridge where they could cross and finally reach the engineer and brakeman. The two men were half-dead with exhaustion.

After that, Kate did not remember the engine puffing away toward the station. She did not remember her mother leading her to bed or piling blankets over her shaking body. She did not remember the gray-and-rose sky of dawn.

The same telegraph that had warned Ogden Station to hold the midnight express sent news of Kate's bravery from city to city. Within days, newspapers all over the nation were calling her the "Iowa heroine."

While Kate lay in bed recovering from that terrible night, every train passing the farmhouse blew its whistle in her honor. Then the people of Iowa awarded her a gold medal, and the railroad gave her one hundred dollars and a lifetime railroad pass.

The nation honored Kate, too. However, the honor most dear to her came from the railroad men themselves. As long as she lived in Moingona, Iowa, they recognized brave Kate in their own special way. Whenever she wanted to ride the Chicago and Northwestern, they stopped the train just for her. A station stop was not good enough. They stopped the train right in front of the little farmhouse on Honey Creek.

In 1900 a new bridge was built across the Des Moines River and named for Kate Shelley. And after her death, the Order of Railway Conductors and Brakemen placed a memorial to their Iowa heroine. "Hers is a deed bound for legend … a story to be told until the last order fades and the last rail rusts."

POETRY

NO MATTER WHERE IT'S GOING

TRAVEL
by Edna St. Vincent Millay

The railroad track is miles away,
    And the day is loud with voices speaking,
Yet there isn't a train goes by all day
    But I hear its whistle shrieking.

All night there isn't a train goes by,
    Though the night is still for sleep and dreaming
But I see its cinders red on the sky,
    And hear its engine steaming.

My heart is warm with the friends I make,
    And better friends I'll not be knowing,
Yet there isn't a train I wouldn't take,
    No matter where it's going.

A MODERN DRAGON

by Rowena Bastin Bennett

A train is a dragon that roars through the dark.
He wriggles his tail as he sends up a spark.
He pierces the night with his one yellow eye,
And all the earth trembles when he rushes by.

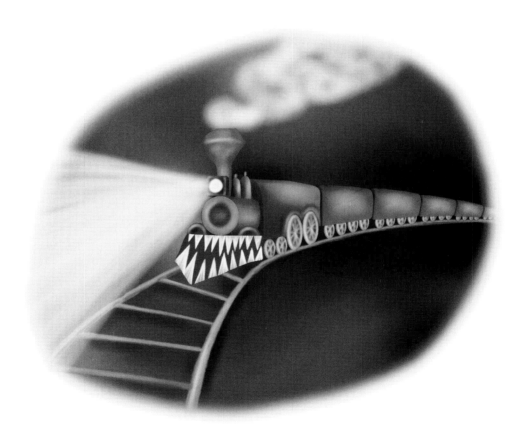

From a Railway Carriage

by Robert Louis Stevenson

Faster than fairies, faster than witches,
Bridges and houses, hedges and ditches;
And charging along like troops in a battle
All through the meadows the horses and cattle:
All of the sights of the hill and the plain
Fly as thick as the driving rain;
And ever again, in the wink of an eye,
Painted stations whistle by.

Here is a child who clambers and scrambles,
All by himself and gathering brambles;
Here is a tramp who stands and gazes;
And there is the green for stringing the daisies!
Here is a cart run away in the road
Lumping along with man and load;
And here is a mill, and there is a river:
Each a glimpse and gone forever!

On a Steamer

by Dorothy W. Baruch

Once
I went for an ocean trip
On a big steamer.

Its whistle blew
With a loud
A woo....

    When dinner time came
    I didn't get off
    No—
        I ate my dinner
        Right on the boat.

When bed time came
I didn't get off
No—
    I went right to sleep
    Right on the boat.

        I had a little room
        With a closet in it
        Where I could hang up my suit
        And my hat
        And my coat.

And when I climbed into bed that night
And put my ear
Down—tight—
Then—
    All at once—
        I could hear
        The engines go
        Way far below
    Throbadoba throbadoba
        Never stopping
        Always throbbing
        Throbadoba throbadoba
        Throba doba dob.

SEA FEVER

by John Masefield

I must go down to the seas again, to the lonely sea and the sky,
And all I ask is a tall ship and a star to steer her by;
And the wheel's kick and the wind's song and the white
    sail's shaking,
And the gray mist on the sea's face, and a gray dawn breaking.

I must go down to the seas again, for the call of the
    running tide
Is a wild call and a clear call that may not be denied;
And all I ask is a windy day with the white clouds flying,
And the flung spray and the blown spume, and the
    seagulls crying.

I must go down to the seas again, to the vagrant gypsy life,
To the gull's way and the whale's way where the wind's like
    a whetted knife;
And all I ask is a merry yarn from a laughing fellow-rover,
And quiet sleep and a sweet dream when the long trick's over.

THE AIRPLANE

by Rowena Bastin Bennett

An airplane has gigantic wings
    But not a feather on her breast;
She only mutters when she sings
    And builds a hangar for a nest.
I love to see her stop and start;
    She has a little motor heart
That beats and throbs and then is still.
    She wears a fan upon her bill.

No eagle flies through sun and rain
    So swiftly as an airplane.
I wish she would come swooping down
    Between the steeples of the town
And lift me right up off my feet
    And take me high above the street,
Then all the other boys might see
    The little speck that would be me.

Cockpit in the Clouds

by Dick Dorrance

Two thousand feet beneath our wheels
The city sprawls across the land
Like heaps of children's blocks outflung,
In tantrums, by a giant hand.
To east a silver spire soars
And seeks to pierce our lower wing.
Above its grasp we drift along,
A tiny, droning, shiny thing.

The noon crowds pack the narrow streets.
The el trains move so slow, so slow.
Amidst their traffic, chaos, life,
The city's busy millions go.
Up here, aloof, we watch them crawl.
In crystal air we seem to poise
Behind our motor's throaty roar—
Down there, we're just another noise.

FLYING

by Kaye Starbird

I like to ride in my uncle's plane,
The one he pilots around the sky.
It's little and blue
And shiny, too,
And looks a lot like a dragonfly.

And once we're high in the summer air
With things below all shrunken in size,
It's easy to dream
How life would seem
If human beings were dragonflies.

The great wide river shrinks to a brook
That slowly winds away to the north,
Where ferries and tugs
Are water bugs
That skitter silently back and forth.

The far away cows are just like ants,
The woods are patches of gray-green moss,
And telegraph lines
Where sunlight shines
Are glinting spider webs strung across.

It's quite exciting to hum through space
And view the world with an insect's eye.
A dragonfly-view
Makes things seem new,
Unless, of course, you're a dragonfly.

ROADS GO EVER ON

by J.R.R. Tolkien

Roads go ever on and on,
    Over rock and under tree,
By caves where sun has never shone,
    By streams that never find the sea;
Over snow by winter sown,
    And through the merry flowers of June,
Over grass and over stone,
    And under mountains in the moon.

ROADS

by Rachel Field

A road might lead to anywhere—
　　To harbor towns and quays,
Or to a witch's pointed house
　　Hidden by bristly trees.
It might lead past the tailor's door,
　　Where he sews with needle and thread
Or by Miss Pim the milliner's,
　　With hats for every head.
It might be a road to a great, dark cave
　　With treasure and gold piled high,
Or a road with a mountain tied to its end
　　Blue-humped against the sky.
Oh, a road might lead you anywhere—
　　To Mexico or Maine.
But then, it might just fool you, and—
　　Lead you back home again!

THE ROAD NOT TAKEN

by Robert Frost

Two roads diverged in a yellow wood,
And sorry I could not travel both
And be one traveler, long I stood
And looked down one as far as I could
To where it bent in the undergrowth;

Then took the other, as just as fair,
And having perhaps the better claim,
Because it was grassy and wanted wear;
Though as for that, the passing there
Had worn them really about the same,

And both that morning equally lay
In leaves no step had trodden black.
Oh, I kept the first for another day!
Yet knowing how way leads on to way,
I doubted if I should ever come back.

I shall be telling this with a sigh
Somewhere ages and ages hence:
Two roads diverged in a wood, and I—
I took the one less traveled by,
And that has made all the difference.

POETRY

AMERICAN THEMES

LITTLE PUPPY

from the Navajo American Indian
transcribed by Hilda Faunce Wetherill

Little puppy with the black spots,
Come and herd the flock with me.
We will climb the red rocks
And from the top we'll see
The tall cliffs, the straight cliffs,
The fluted cliffs,
Where the eagles live.
We'll see the dark rocks,
The smooth rocks,
That hold the rain to give us
Water, when we eat our bread and meat,
When the sun is high.
Little spotted dog of mine,
Come and spend the day with me.
When the sun is going down
Behind the pointed hill,
We will follow home the flock.
They will lead the way
To the hogans where the fires burn
And the square cornbread is in the ashes,
Waiting our return.

THE GRASS ON THE MOUNTAIN

from the Paiute American Indian
transcribed by Mary Austin

Oh, long long
The snow has possessed the mountains.

The deer have come down and the big-horn,
They have followed the Sun to the south
To feed on the mesquite pods and the bunch grass.
Loud are the thunderdrums
In the tents of the mountains.
Oh, long long
Have we eaten chia seeds
And dried deer's flesh of the summer killing.
We are wearied of our huts
And the smoky smell of our garments.

We are sick with desire of the sun
And the grass on the mountain.

A Song of Greatness

a Chippewa Indian song
transcribed by Mary Austin

When I hear the old men
Telling of heroes,
Telling of great deeds
Of ancient days,
When I hear that telling
Then I think within me
I too, am one of these.

When I hear the people
Praising great ones,
Then I know that I too
Shall be esteemed,
I too when my time comes
Shall do mightily.

THIS LAND IS YOUR LAND

by Woody Guthrie

As I was walking that ribbon of highway
I saw above me that endless skyway.
I saw below me that golden valley
This land was made for you and me.

This land is your land, this land is my land,
From California to the New York island.
From the redwood forest to the Gulf Stream waters,
This land was made for you and me.

AMERICA THE BEAUTIFUL
by Katharine Lee Bates

O beautiful for spacious skies,
    For amber waves of grain,
For purple mountain majesties
    Above the fruited plain!
      America! America!
    God shed His grace on thee,
And crown thy good with brotherhood
    From sea to shining sea!

THE STAR-SPANGLED BANNER
by Francis Scott Key

O say, can you see, by the dawn's early light,
What so proudly we hailed at the twilight's last gleaming?
Whose broad stripes and bright stars, through the
    perilous fight,
O'er the ramparts we watched were so gallantly streaming!
And the rockets' red glare, the bombs bursting in air,
Gave proof through the night that our flag was still there:
O say, does that star-spangled banner yet wave
O'er the land of the free and the home of the brave?

COLUMBUS

by Joaquin Miller

Behind him lay the gray Azores,
    Behind the Gates of Hercules;
Before him not the ghost of shores,
    Before him only shoreless seas.
The good mate said: "Now must we pray,
    For lo! the very stars are gone.
Brave Admiral, speak, what shall I say?"
    "Why, say 'Sail on! sail on! and on!'"

"My men grow mutinous day by day;
    My men grow ghastly wan and weak."
The stout mate thought of home; a spray
    Of salt wave washed his swarthy cheek.
"What shall I say, brave Admiral, say,
    If we sight naught but seas at dawn?"
"Why, you shall say at break of day,
    'Sail on! sail on! sail on! and on!'"

They sailed and sailed, as winds might blow,
    Until at last the blanched mate said,
"Why, now not even God would know
    Should I and all my men fall dead.
These very winds forget their way,
    For God from these dread seas is gone.
Now speak, brave Admiral, speak and say"—
    He said: "Sail on! sail on! and on!"

They sailed. They sailed. Then spoke the mate:
    "This mad sea shows his teeth tonight.
He curls his lip, he lies in wait,
    With lifted teeth, as if to bite!
Brave Admiral, say but one good word:
    What shall we do when hope is gone?"
The words leapt like a leaping sword:
    "Sail on! sail on! sail on! and on!"

Then, pale and worn, he kept his deck,
    And peered through darkness. Ah, that night
Of all dark nights! And then a speck—
    A light! a light! a light! a light!
It grew, a starlit flag unfurled!
    It grew to be Time's burst of dawn.
He gained a world; he gave that world
    Its grandest lesson: "On! sail on!"

George Washington

by Rosemary and Stephen Vincent Benét

Sing hey! for bold George Washington,
That jolly British tar,
King George's famous admiral
From Hull to Zanzibar!
No—wait a minute—something's wrong—
George *wished* to sail the foam.
But, when his mother thought, aghast,
Of Georgie shinning up a mast,
Her tears and protests flowed so fast
That George remained at home.

Sing ho! for grave Washington,
The staid Virginia squire,
Who farms his fields and hunts his hounds
And aims at nothing higher!
Stop, stop, it's going wrong again!
George *liked* to live on farms,
But, when the Colonies agreed
They could and should and would be freed,
They called on George to do the deed
And George cried "Shoulder arms!"

Sing ha! for Emperor Washington,
That hero of renown,
Who freed his land from Britain's rule
To win a golden crown!
No, no, that's what George *might* have won
But didn't, for he said,
"There's not much point about a king,
They're pretty but they're apt to sting
And, as for crowns—the heavy thing
Would only hurt my head."

Sing ho! for our George Washington!
(At last I've got it straight.)
The first in war, the first in peace,
The goodly and the great.
But, when you think about him now,
From here to Valley Forge,
Remember this—he might have been
A highly different specimen,
And, where on earth would we be, then?
I'm glad that George was George.

ABRAHAM LINCOLN

by Mildred Plew Meigs

Remember he was poor and country-bred;
   His face was lined; he walked with awkward gait.
Smart people laughed at him sometimes and said,
   "How can so very plain a man be great?"

Remember he was humble, used to toil.
   Strong arms he had to build a shack, a fence,
Long legs to tramp the woods, to plow the soil,
   A head chuck full of backwoods common sense.

Remember all he ever had he earned.
   He walked in time through stately White House doors;
But all he knew of men and life he learned
   In little backwoods cabins, country stores.

Remember that his eyes could light with fun;
   That wisdom, courage, set his name apart;
But when the rest is duly said and done,
   Remember that men loved him for his heart.

I Hear America Singing

by Walt Whitman

I hear America singing, the varied carols I hear,
Those of mechanics, each one singing his as it should be,
    blithe and strong.
The carpenter singing his as he measures his plank or beam,
The mason singing as he makes ready for work, or leaves
    off work,
The boatman singing what belongs to him in the boat, the
    deckhand singing on the steamboat deck,
The shoemaker singing as he sits on his bench, the hatter
    singing as he stands,

The woodcutter's song, the ploughboy's on his way in the
    morning, or at noon intermission, or at sundown,
The delicious singing of the mother, or of the young wife at
    work, or of the girl sewing or washing,
Each singing what belongs to him or her and to none else,
The day what belongs to the day—at night the party of young
    fellows, robust, friendly,
Singing with open mouths their strong, melodious songs.

I, Too

by Langston Hughes

I, too, sing America.

I am the darker brother.
They send me to eat in the kitchen
When company comes,
But I laugh,
And eat well,
And grow strong.

Tomorrow,
I'll be at the table
When company comes.
Nobody'll dare
Say to me,
"Eat in the kitchen,"
Then.

Besides,
They'll see how beautiful I am
And be ashamed—

I, too, am America.

THE NEW COLOSSUS

by Emma Lazarus

Not like the brazen giant of Greek fame,
With conquering limbs astride from land to land;
Here at our sea-washed, sunset gates shall stand
A mighty woman with a torch, whose flame
Is the imprisoned lightning, and her name
Mother of Exiles. From her beacon-hand
Glows world-wide welcome; her mild eyes command
The air-bridged harbor that twin cities frame.
"Keep, ancient lands, your storied pomp!" cries she
With silent lips. "Give me your tired, your poor,
Your huddled masses yearning to breathe free,
The wretched refuse of your teeming shore.
Send these, the homeless, tempest-tost to me,
I lift my lamp beside the golden door!"

TEXT CREDITS AND SOURCES

Stories

"The Real Sherlock Holmes" by Irving Wallace from THE READER'S DIGEST TREASURY FOR YOUNG READERS, copyright © 1963, published by Readers Digest and Random House, Inc. Reprinted with the permission of the Estate of Irving Wallace.

"A Ride in the Night" by Katharine E. Wilkie. Reprinted with the permission of Aladdin Paperbacks, an imprint of Simon & Schuster Children's Publishing Division from WILL CLARK: BOY ADVENTURER by Katharine E. Wilkie. Copyright © 1963 The Bobbs-Merrill Company; copyright © renewed 1991 Katharine E. Wilkie.

"Run, Kate Shelly, Run" by Julia Pferdehirt, copyright © 1999 by Julia Pferdehirt. Reprinted by permission of the author.

"Young Frederick Douglass: The Slave Who Learned to Read" by Linda Walvoord Girard. Copyright © 1994 by Linda Walvoord Girard. Original illustrations by Colin Bootman. Adapted and reillustrated by permission of Albert Whitman & Company. All rights reserved.

Poems

"George Washington" by Stephen Vincent Benet from A BOOK OF AMERICANS by Rosemary and Stephen Vincent Benet, Copyright © 1933 by Rosemary and Stephen Vincent Benet, copyright renewed © 1961 by Rosemary Carr Benet. Reprinted by permission of Brandt & Hochman Literary Agents, Inc.

"I, Too" From THE COLLECTED POEMS OF LANGSTON HUGHES by Langston Hughes, copyright © 1994 by The Estate of Langston Hughes. Used by permission of Alfred A. Knopf, a division of Random House, Inc.

"Roads Go Ever On" from THE HOBBIT by J.R.R. Tolkien. Copyright © 1966 by J.R.R. Tolkien. Reprinted by permission of Houghton Mifflin Company. All Rights Reserved.

"The Road Not Taken" by Robert Frost from THE POETRY OF ROBERT FROST edited by Edward Connery Lathem. Copyright © 1916, © 1969 by Henry Holt and Co., copyright 1944 by Robert Frost. Reprinted by permission of Henry Holt and Company, LLC.

"A Song of Greatness" from THE CHILDREN SING IN THE FAR WEST by Mary Austin. Copyright 1928 by Mary Austin; copyright renewed © 1956 by Kenneth Chapman and Mary C. Wheelwright. Reprinted by permission of Houghton Mifflin Company. All rights reserved.

Other selections:

Shakespeare's *The Tempest* and *A Midsummer Night's Dream* adapted from *Tales from Shakespeare* by Charles and Mary Lamb (1807) and *The Progressive Road to Reading: Book Five* ed. Georgine Burchill et al (New York: Silver, Burdett and Co., 1909)

"The Red-Headed League" (1891) and "The Adventure of the Blue Carbuncle" (1892) by Sir Arthur Conan Doyle, adapted by Vanessa Wright

While every care has been taken to trace and acknowledge copyright, the editors tender their apologies for any accidental infringement when copyright has proven untraceable. They would be pleased to include the appropriate acknowledgment in any subsequent edition of this publication.